FOUNTAS & PINNELL

Benchmark Assessment System **1**

Irene C. Fountas • Gay Su Pinnell

Heinemann
Portsmouth NH

Heinemann
361 Hanover St.
Portsmouth, NH 03801-3912
www.heinemann.com

Offices and agents throughout the world.

Fountas & Pinnell Benchmark Assessment System 1
Assessment Forms

Copyright © 2011, 2008 by Irene C. Fountas and Gay Su Pinnell

cover: (top) Andrew Swaine, (middle/bottom) Mike Swendner
page vii: (top/middle) Andrew Swaine, (bottom) Mike Swendner
page 201: (top/bottom) Mike Swendner, (middle) Andrew Swaine
page 211: (top/middle) Mike Swendner, (bottom) Andrew Swaine
page 389: (top/middle/bottom) Mike Swendner

ISBN10: 0-325-02774-9
ISBN13: 978-0-325-02774-6

Printed in Shenzhen, China
0611/11003634

2 3 4 5 6 7 8 RRD 15 14 13 12 11

Table of Contents

Optional Assessments

Recording Forms

The following section includes the Recording Forms you will need to code and score a student's reading of each benchmark book. You will want to photocopy the forms in advance and keep them accessible while you are conducting your benchmark assessment conferences. Expanded versions of the Recording Forms with extra spacing for coding are also available on the *Forms CD-ROM*.

Student _____ Grade _____ Date _____

Teacher _____ School _____

Recording Form
Part One: Oral Reading

Place the book in front of the student. Read the title and introduction.

Introduction: In this story, two girls tell all the things they like to do together. Read to find out what they like to do. Point under each word as you read.

Summary of Scores:	
Accuracy	_____
Self-correction	_____
Fluency	_____
Comprehension	_____
Writing	_____

Sources of Information Used

Page	Text	*Best Friends* Level A, RW: 32, E: 4	E	SC	E			SC		
					M	S	V	M	S	V
2	We like to run.									
4	We like to dance.									
6	We like to swing.									
8	We like to climb.									
10	We like to slide.									
12	We like to ride.									
14	We like to paint.									
16	We **love** to read.									
		Total								

© 2011, 2008 by Irene C. Fountas and Gay Su Pinnell. Portsrrouth, NH: Heinemann. This page may be photocopied.

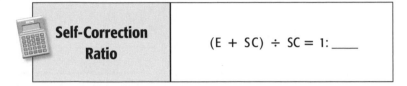

Accuracy Rate	Errors	4 or more	3	2	1	0
	%	Below 90%	91%	94%	97%	100%

Self-Correction Ratio	(E + SC) ÷ SC = 1: ____

Part Two: Comprehension Conversation

Have a conversation with the student, noting the key understandings the student expresses. Use prompts as needed to stimulate discussion of understandings the student does not express. It is not necessary to use every prompt for each book. Score for evidence of all understandings expressed—with or without a prompt. Circle the number in the score column that reflects the level of understanding demonstrated.

Teacher: Talk about what happened in this story.

Comprehension Scoring Key

0   Reflects **unsatisfactory** understanding of the text. Either does not respond or talks off the topic.

1   Reflects **limited** understanding of the text. Mentions a few facts or ideas but does not express the important information or ideas.

2   Reflects **satisfactory** understanding of the text. Includes important information and ideas but neglects other key understandings.

3   Reflects **excellent** understanding of the text. Includes almost all important information and main ideas.

Key Understandings	Prompts	Score
Within the Text There are lots of different things the girls like to do together. (Gives 2–3 examples such as run, dance, swing, climb, slide, ride, paint, and read.) *Note any additional understandings:*	Tell some things the girls like to do together. Can you tell more things they like to do together?	0 1 2 3
Beyond and About the Text The girls like to do things with each other. The girls like to read more than they like to do other things. The author made the the word *love* darker to show they liked reading best. The author said *love* instead of *like* to show they liked reading best. *Note any additional understandings:*	How can you tell these girls are best friends? Of all the things the girls do together, what's their favorite thing to do? Why? The author told about all the things the girls liked to do. Look at the last page. Why did the author make the word *love* very dark?	0 1 2 3

Guide to Total Score
6–7 **Excellent** Comprehension
5   **Satisfactory** Comprehension
4   **Limited** Comprehension
0–3 **Unsatisfactory** Comprehension

Subtotal Score: _____ /6
Add 1 for any additional understandings: _____ /1
Total Score: _____ /7

Part Three: Writing About Reading (optional)

Read the writing/drawing prompt below to the student. You can also cut the prompt on the dotted line and give it to the child. Specify the amount of time for the student to complete the task on a separate sheet of paper. (See *Assessment Guide* for more information.)

Writing About Reading Scoring Key
0 Reflects **no** understanding of the text.
1 Reflects **very limited** understanding of the text.
2 Reflects **partial** understanding of the text.
3 Reflects **excellent** understanding of the text.

Write about what the two girls like to do together. You can draw a picture to go with your writing.

| Student _____ | Grade _____ | Date _____ |
| Teacher _____ | School _____ |

Recording Form

Part One: Oral Reading

Place the book in front of the student. Read the title and introduction.

Introduction: This boy is telling all the things he can do at the park with his dad. Read to find out what he says he can do. Point under each word as you read.

Summary of Scores:

Accuracy	_____
Self-correction	_____
Fluency	_____
Comprehension	_____
Writing	_____

Sources of Information Used

Page	Text	*At the Park* Level A, RW: 24, E: 3	E	SC	E			SC		
					M	S	V	M	S	V
2	I can ride.									
4	I can kick.									
6	I can catch.									
8	I can jump.									
10	I can swing.									
12	I can slide.									
14	I can run.									
16	I can hide.									
		Total								

Accuracy Rate	Errors	3 or more	2	1	0
	%	Below 90%	92%	96%	100%

Self-Correction Ratio	(E + SC) ÷ SC = 1:____

Part Two: Comprehension Conversation

Have a conversation with the student, noting the key understandings the student expresses. Use prompts as needed to stimulate discussion of understandings the student does not express. It is not necessary to use every prompt for each book. Score for evidence of all understandings expressed—with or without a prompt. Circle the number in the score column that reflects the level of understanding demonstrated.

Teacher: Talk about what you learned in this book.

Comprehension Scoring Key

0   Reflects **unsatisfactory** understanding of the text. Either does not respond or talks off the topic.

1   Reflects **limited** understanding of the text. Mentions a few facts or ideas but does not express the important information or ideas.

2   Reflects **satisfactory** understanding of the text. Includes important information and ideas but neglects other key understandings.

3   Reflects **excellent** understanding of the text. Includes almost all important information and main ideas.

Key Understandings	Prompts	Score
Within the Text The boy can do lots of things at the park. (Gives 2–3 examples such as ride, kick, catch, jump, swing, slide, run, and hide.) *Note any additional understandings:*	Talk about what things the boy can do at the park.	0 1 2 3
Beyond and About the Text It's fun to (gives opinion or examples from own life) at the park. Some other things they could do at the park are (gives examples). Some people like to go to the park because they can (be outside and play, have picnics, etc). The boy really likes to go to the park with his dad because (gives any reasonable explanation). The boy and his dad are smiling. *Note any additional understandings:*	What are some fun things to do at the park? Can you think of some other things that the boy and his dad could do at the park? Why do people like to go to the park? Why do you think the boy likes to go to the park? Look at pages 14 and 15. How does the picture help you know the boy and his dad like to go to the park?	0 1 2 3

Guide to Total Score

6–7 Excellent Comprehension

5   Satisfactory Comprehension

4   Limited Comprehension

0–3 Unsatisfactory Comprehension

Subtotal Score: _____ /6

Add 1 for any additional understandings: _____ /1

Total Score: _____ /7

Part Three: Writing About Reading *(optional)*

Read the writing/drawing prompt below to the student. You can also cut the prompt on the dotted line and give it to the child. Specify the amount of time for the student to complete the task on a separate sheet of paper. (See *Assessment Guide* for more information.)

Writing About Reading Scoring Key

0 Reflects **no** understanding of the text.

1 Reflects **very limited** understanding of the text.

2 Reflects **partial** understanding of the text.

3 Reflects **excellent** understanding of the text.

Write about what the boy can do at the park. You can draw a picture to go with your writing.

© 2011, 2008 by Irene C. Fountas and Gay Su Pinnell, Portsmouth, NH: Heinemann. This page may be photocopied.

Student _____   Grade _____   Date _____

Teacher _____   School _____

Recording Form
Part One: Oral Reading

Place the book in front of the student. Read the title and introduction.

Introduction: This girl has a little dog. Read to find out all the things her little dog likes to do with her. Point under each word as you read.

Summary of Scores:	
Accuracy	_____
Self-correction	_____
Fluency	_____
Comprehension	_____
Writing	_____

Sources of Information Used

Page	Text — *My Little Dog* Level B, RW: 55, E: 6	E	SC	E			SC		
				M	S	V	M	S	V
2	My little dog likes to sleep with me.								
4	My little dog likes to eat with me.								
6	My little dog likes to run with me.								
8	He likes to play with me.								
10	He likes to ride with me.								
	Subtotal								

Part One: Oral Reading *continued*

Sources of Information Used

Page	Text	E	SC	E			SC		
				M	S	V	M	S	V
12	He likes to jump with me.								
14	My little dog likes to read with me.								
16	My little dog likes me!								
	Subtotal								
	Total								

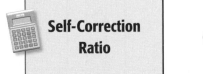

Accuracy Rate	Errors	6 or more	5	4	3	2	1	0
	%	Below 90%	91%	93%	95%	96%	98%	100%

Self-Correction Ratio	(E + SC) ÷ SC = 1: ____

Recording Forms

Part Two: Comprehension Conversation

Have a conversation with the student, noting the key understandings the student expresses. Use prompts as needed to stimulate discussion of understandings the student does not express. It is not necessary to use every prompt for each book. Score for evidence of all understandings expressed—with or without a prompt. Circle the number in the score column that reflects the level of understanding demonstrated.

Teacher: Talk about what happened in this story.

<table>
<tr><td colspan="2">**Comprehension Scoring Key**</td></tr>
<tr><td>**0**</td><td>Reflects **unsatisfactory** understanding of the text. Either does not respond or talks off the topic.</td></tr>
<tr><td>**1**</td><td>Reflects **limited** understanding of the text. Mentions a few facts or ideas but does not express the important information or ideas.</td></tr>
<tr><td>**2**</td><td>Reflects **satisfactory** understanding of the text. Includes important information and ideas but neglects other key understandings.</td></tr>
<tr><td>**3**</td><td>Reflects **excellent** understanding of the text. Includes almost all important information and main ideas.</td></tr>
</table>

Key Understandings	Prompts	Score
Within the Text The girl is telling about her little dog and the things he can do. The little dog likes to do lots of things with her. (Gives 2–3 examples such as sleep, eat, run, play, ride, jump, and read.) *Note any additional understandings:*	What did the girl tell about in the book? Tell some of the things this little dog likes to do with the girl.	0 1 2 3
Beyond and About the Text The little dog likes to do lots of things and probably likes to do other things too (gives examples). The girl is really proud of (or loves) her dog. This dog is like my dog (or makes any personal connection). The pictures show that they like each other because (any reasons based on any picture; for example, on page 16 she is smiling and petting the dog and the dog is licking her). *Note any additional understandings:*	What other things do you think the little dog likes to do with the girl? How do you think the girl feels about her little dog? Did this book remind you of anything? Look at page 16. How does the picture show you that the little girl and the dog like each other?	0 1 2 3

Guide to Total Score

6–7 **Excellent** Comprehension

5   **Satisfactory** Comprehension

4   **Limited** Comprehension

0–3 **Unsatisfactory** Comprehension

Subtotal Score: _____ /6

Add 1 for any additional understandings: _____ /1

Total Score: _____ /7

Part Three: Writing About Reading (optional)

Read the writing/drawing prompt below to the student. You can also cut the prompt on the dotted line and give it to the child. Specify the amount of time for the student to complete the task on a separate sheet of paper. (See *Assessment Guide* for more information.)

Writing About Reading Scoring Key

0 Reflects **no** understanding of the text.

1 Reflects **very limited** understanding of the text.

2 Reflects **partial** understanding of the text.

3 Reflects **excellent** understanding of the text.

- -

Write about three things the little dog likes to do. You can draw a picture to go with your writing.

© 2011, 2008 by Irene C. Fountas and Gay Su Pinnell. Portsmouth, NH: Heinemann. This page may be photocopied.

Student _____   Grade _____   Date _____

Teacher _____   School _____

Recording Form
Part One: Oral Reading

Place the book in front of the student. Read the title and introduction.

Introduction: In this book, a girl is playing with lots of different things. Read about all the things she likes to play with. Point under each word as you read.

Summary of Scores:	
Accuracy	_____
Self-correction	_____
Fluency	_____
Comprehension	_____
Writing	_____

Sources of Information Used

Page	Text *Playing* Level B, RW: 56, E: 6	E	SC	E			SC		
				M	S	V	M	S	V
2	I like to play with a truck.								
4	I like to play with a car.								
6	I like to play with the ball.								
8	I like to play with my doll.								
10	I like to play with a train.								
	Subtotal								

Part One: Oral Reading *continued*

Sources of Information Used

Page	Text	E	SC	E			SC		
				M	S	V	M	S	V
12	I like to play with the plane.								
14	I like to play with a boat.								
16	I like to play with my dog!								
	Subtotal								
	Total								

Accuracy Rate	Errors	6 or more	5	4	3	2	1	0
	%	Below 90%	91%	93%	95%	96%	98%	100%

Self-Correction Ratio	(E + SC) ÷ SC = 1: _____

Part Two: Comprehension Conversation

Have a conversation with the student, noting the key understandings the student expresses. Use prompts as needed to stimulate discussion of understandings the student does not express. It is not necessary to use every prompt for each book. Score for evidence of all understandings expressed—with or without a prompt. Circle the number in the score column that reflects the level of understanding demonstrated.

Comprehension Scoring Key

0 Reflects **unsatisfactory** understanding of the text. Either does not respond or talks off the topic.

1 Reflects **limited** understanding of the text. Mentions a few facts or ideas but does not express the important information or ideas.

2 Reflects **satisfactory** understanding of the text. Includes important information and ideas but neglects other key understandings.

3 Reflects **excellent** understanding of the text. Includes almost all important information and main ideas.

Teacher: Talk about what you learned in this book.

Key Understandings	Prompts	Score
Within the Text The girl likes to play with lots of different things. (Gives 3–4 examples such as truck, car, ball, doll, train, plane, boat, and dog.) *Note any additional understandings:*	Tell some of the things the girl likes to play with. What else can you say about what the girl likes to do?	0 1 2 3
Beyond and About the Text Some of the things the girl likes to play with are toys, but a dog is not a toy. I like (or have) some of the same things the girl likes to play with. The girl is having fun in this story. The last thing she plays with is the dog because everything else is a toy, but the dog is alive and can play with her. *Note any additional understandings:*	What do you notice about the things the girl likes to play with? Does this book make you think of things you like to play with? How do you think the girl was feeling in this story? The girl played with the dog last. How is the dog different from all the other things?	0 1 2 3

Guide to Total Score

6–7 **Excellent** Comprehension

5 **Satisfactory** Comprehension

4 **Limited** Comprehension

0–3 **Unsatisfactory** Comprehension

Subtotal Score: _____ /6

Add 1 for any additional understandings: _____ /1

Total Score: _____ /7

Part Three: Writing About Reading *(optional)*

Read the writing/drawing prompt below to the student. You can also cut the prompt on the dotted line and give it to the child. Specify the amount of time for the student to complete the task on a separate sheet of paper. (See *Assessment Guide* for more information.)

Writing About Reading Scoring Key

0 Reflects **no** understanding of the text.

1 Reflects **very limited** understanding of the text.

2 Reflects **partial** understanding of the text.

3 Reflects **excellent** understanding of the text.

Write about three things the girl likes to play with. You can draw a picture to go with your writing.

Student _____   Grade _____   Date _____

Teacher _____   School _____

Recording Form
Part One: Oral Reading

Place the book in front of the student. Read the title and introduction.

Introduction: Socks the cat was sleeping in lots of different places, and the girl wanted her to wake up. Read to find out what makes Socks wake up.

Summary of Scores:	
Accuracy	_____
Self-correction	_____
Fluency	_____
Comprehension	_____
Writing	_____

Sources of Information Used

Page	Text	E	SC	E M	E S	E V	SC M	SC S	SC V
	Socks Level C, RW: 79, E: 9								
2	Socks was sleeping on the bed. "Wake up, Socks!" I said.								
4	Socks was sleeping on my chair. I said, "Wake up, Socks!"								
6	She was sleeping on the couch. "Wake up, Socks!" I said.								
	Subtotal								

Part One: Oral Reading *continued*

© 2011, 2008 by Irene C. Fountas and Gay Su Pinnell. Portsmouth, NH: Heinemann. This page may be photocopied.

Sources of Information Used

Page	Text	E	SC	E			SC		
				M	S	V	M	S	V
8	She was sleeping on the rug. I said, "Wake up, Socks!"								
10	She was sleeping by the window. I said, "Socks, wake up!"								
12	Socks was sleeping by the door. "Wake up!" I said.								
14	Socks was sleeping under the table.								
	Subtotal								

Part One: Oral Reading *continued*

Sources of Information Used

Page	Text	E	SC	E			SC		
				M	S	V	M	S	V
14 *cont.*	"I can wake Socks up," I said.								
16	Purr								
	Subtotal								
	Total								

Accuracy Rate	**Errors**	**9 or more**	**8**	**7**	**6**	**5**	**4**	**3**	**2**	**1**	**0**
	%	Below 90%	90%	91%	92%	94%	95%	96%	97%	99%	100%

Self-Correction Ratio

(E + SC) ÷ SC = 1: _____

Fluency Score   0   1   2   3

Fluency Scoring Key

0 Reads primarily word-by-word with occasional but infrequent or inappropriate phrasing; no smooth or expressive interpretation, irregular pausing, and no attention to author's meaning or punctuation; no stress or inappropriate stress, and slow rate.

1 Reads primarily in two-word phrases with some three- and four-word groups and some word-by-word reading; almost no smooth, expressive interpretation or pausing guided by author's meaning and punctuation; almost no stress or inappropriate stress, with slow rate most of the time.

2 Reads primarily in three- or four-word phrase groups; some smooth, expressive interpretation and pausing guided by author's meaning and punctuation; mostly appropriate stress and rate with some slowdowns.

3 Reads primarily in larger, meaningful phrases or word groups; mostly smooth, expressive interpretation and pausing guided by author's meaning and punctuation; appropriate stress and rate with only a few slowdowns.

Part Two: Comprehension Conversation

Have a conversation with the student, noting the key understandings the student expresses. Use prompts as needed to stimulate discussion of understandings the student does not express. It is not necessary to use every prompt for each book. Score for evidence of all understandings expressed—with or without a prompt. Circle the number in the score column that reflects the level of understanding demonstrated.

<table>
<tr><td>Comprehension Scoring Key</td></tr>
<tr><td>0 Reflects unsatisfactory understanding of the text. Either does not respond or talks off the topic.</td></tr>
<tr><td>1 Reflects limited understanding of the text. Mentions a few facts or ideas but does not express the important information or ideas.</td></tr>
<tr><td>2 Reflects satisfactory understanding of the text. Includes important information and ideas but neglects other key understandings.</td></tr>
<tr><td>3 Reflects excellent understanding of the text. Includes almost all important information and main ideas.</td></tr>
</table>

Teacher: Talk about what happened in this story.

Key Understandings	Prompts	Score
Within the Text Socks the cat was sleeping in many different places in the house. A girl was trying to wake Socks up but she would not wake up. The girl got Socks to wake up with some food. *Note any additional understandings:*	Talk about what Socks was doing in this story. What happened when the girl told Socks to wake up? What happened at the end?	0 1 2 3
Beyond and About the Text Socks was a sleepy (or lazy) cat. Socks woke up because she wanted to eat the food. The picture showed that Socks was lazy because she was sleeping. The picture on the last page showed Socks saying "Purr" because she liked the food and was lazy and sleepy. *Note any additional understandings:*	Tell what Socks is like. Why did Socks wake up? How does the author show what Socks was like? How does the last page show that Socks was happy?	0 1 2 3

Guide to Total Score

6–7 **Excellent** Comprehension

5   **Satisfactory** Comprehension

4   **Limited** Comprehension

0–3 **Unsatisfactory** Comprehension

Subtotal Score: _____ /6

Add 1 for any additional understandings: _____ /1

Total Score: _____ /7

Part Three: Writing About Reading *(optional)*

Read the writing/drawing prompt below to the student. You can also cut the prompt on the dotted line and give it to the child. Specify the amount of time for the student to complete the task on a separate sheet of paper. (See *Assessment Guide* for more information.)

<table>
<tr><td>Writing About Reading Scoring Key</td></tr>
<tr><td>0 Reflects no understanding of the text.</td></tr>
<tr><td>1 Reflects very limited understanding of the text.</td></tr>
<tr><td>2 Reflects partial understanding of the text.</td></tr>
<tr><td>3 Reflects excellent understanding of the text.</td></tr>
</table>

Write about three places that Socks liked to sleep. You can draw a picture to go with your writing.

Student _____   Grade _____   Date _____

Teacher _____   School _____

Recording Form

Part One: Oral Reading

Place the book in front of the student. Read the title and introduction.

Introduction: A boy is helping his mother shop for food in the market. Read
to see what the boy gets for his mom and what she gets for him.

Summary of Scores:	
Accuracy	_____
Self-correction	_____
Fluency	_____
Comprehension	_____
Writing	_____

Sources of Information Used

Page	Text *Shopping* Level C, RW: 96, E: 11	E	SC	E M	E S	E V	SC M	SC S	SC V
2	"Get some milk," said Mom.								
3	I put the milk in the cart.								
4	"Get some apples," said Mom.								
5	I put the apples in the cart.								
6	"Get some bananas," Mom said.								
7	I put the bananas in the cart.								
	Subtotal								

Part One: Oral Reading *continued*

Sources of Information Used

Page	Text	E	SC	E			SC		
				M	S	V	M	S	V
8	Mom said, "Get some oranges."								
9	I put some oranges in the cart.								
10	"Get some carrots," Mom said.								
11	I put the carrots in the cart.								
12	"Get some tomatoes," Mom said.								
13	I put the tomatoes in the cart.								
14	"Get some bread," said Mom.								
	Subtotal								

Part One: Oral Reading *continued*

Sources of Information Used

Page	Text	E	SC	E			SC		
				M	S	V	M	S	V
15	I put the bread in the cart.								
16	"Get some cookies," I said. Mom put the cookies in the cart.								
	Subtotal								
	Total								

Accuracy Rate	Errors	11 or more	10	9	8	7	6	5	4	3	2	1	0
	%	Below 90%	90%	91%	92%	93%	94%	95%	96%	97%	98%	99%	100%

Self-Correction Ratio

(E + SC) ÷ SC = 1: ____

Fluency Score 0 1 2 3

Fluency Scoring Key

0 Reads primarily word-by-word with occasional but infrequent or inappropriate phrasing; no smooth or expressive interpretation, irregular pausing, and no attention to author's meaning or punctuation; no stress or inappropriate stress, and slow rate.

1 Reads primarily in two-word phrases with some three- and four-word groups and some word-by-word reading; almost no smooth, expressive interpretation or pausing guided by author's meaning and punctuation; almost no stress or inappropriate stress, with slow rate most of the time.

2 Reads primarily in three- or four-word phrase groups; some smooth, expressive interpretation and pausing guided by author's meaning and punctuation; mostly appropriate stress and rate with some slowdowns.

3 Reads primarily in larger, meaningful phrases or word groups; mostly smooth, expressive interpretation and pausing guided by author's meaning and punctuation; appropriate stress and rate with only a few slowdowns.

Part Two: Comprehension Conversation

Have a conversation with the student, noting the key understandings the student expresses. Use prompts as needed to stimulate discussion of understandings the student does not express. It is not necessary to use every prompt for each book. Score for evidence of all understandings expressed—with or without a prompt. Circle the number in the score column that reflects the level of understanding demonstrated.

Teacher: Talk about what you learned in this book.

Comprehension Scoring Key	
0	Reflects **unsatisfactory** understanding of the text. Either does not respond or talks off the topic.
1	Reflects **limited** understanding of the text. Mentions a few facts or ideas but does not express the important information or ideas.
2	Reflects **satisfactory** understanding of the text. Includes important information and ideas but neglects other key understandings.
3	Reflects **excellent** understanding of the text. Includes almost all important information and main ideas.

Key Understandings	Prompts	Score
Within the Text The boy got everything his mom told him to get. (Gives 2–3 examples such as milk, apples, bananas, oranges, carrots, tomatoes, and bread.) At the end, the mom got the cookies when the boy told her to. *Note any additional understandings:*	Tell some of the things the mom told the boy to get. What happened at the end?	0 1 2 3
Beyond and About the Text The boy liked to help his mom shop. The mom got the cookies because the boy had been a good helper. The boy thought it was funny (or was happy) that his mom got the cookies. The last page showed Mom getting the cookies because it was what the boy wanted. *Note any additional understandings:*	Why do you think the boy was getting everything his mom told him to get? Why do you think his mom got the cookies? How do you think the boy felt when his mom got the cookies? Look at the last page. How do you know that Mom thought the boy had done a good job?	0 1 2 3

Guide to Total Score	
6–7	**Excellent** Comprehension
5	**Satisfactory** Comprehension
4	**Limited** Comprehension
0–3	**Unsatisfactory** Comprehension

Subtotal Score: _____ /6

Add 1 for any additional understandings: _____ /1

Total Score: _____ /7

Part Three: Writing About Reading *(optional)*

Read the writing/drawing prompt below to the student. You can also cut the prompt on the dotted line and give it to the child. Specify the amount of time for the student to complete the task on a separate sheet of paper. (See *Assessment Guide* for more information.)

Writing About Reading Scoring Key	
0	Reflects **no** understanding of the text.
1	Reflects **very limited** understanding of the text.
2	Reflects **partial** understanding of the text.
3	Reflects **excellent** understanding of the text.

Write about how the boy and his mom helped each other when they were shopping. You can draw a picture to go with your writing.

Student _____   Grade _____   Date _____

Teacher _____   School _____

Recording Form

Part One: Oral Reading

Summary of Scores:	
Accuracy	_____
Self-correction	_____
Fluency	_____
Comprehension	_____
Writing	_____

Place the book in front of the student. Read the title and introduction.

Introduction: In this story, each animal went into a little house and said, "What a nice little house!" Read to find out what happened when all the animals went in.

Sources of Information Used

Page	Text *The Nice Little House* Level D, RW: 129, E: 14	E	SC	E M	E S	E V	SC M	SC S	SC V
2	The horse went in the little house. "What a nice little house!" said the horse.								
4	The cow went in the little house. "What a nice little house!" said the cow.								
6	The pig went in the little house. The pig said, "What a nice little house!"								
8	The chicken went in the little house.								
	Subtotal								

Part One: Oral Reading *continued*

Sources of Information Used

Page	Text	E	SC	E			SC		
				M	S	V	M	S	V
8 *cont.*	"What a nice little house!" she said.								
10	The duck went in the little house. She said, "What a nice little house!"								
12	The skunk went in the little house. Then . . .								
14	The horse went out of the little house. The cow went out of the little house.								
15	The pig went out of the little house. The chicken went								
	Subtotal								

Recording Forms

Part One: Oral Reading *continued*

Sources of Information Used

Page	Text	E	SC	E			SC		
				M	S	V	M	S	V
15 *cont.*	out of the little house. The duck went out of the little house.								
16	"What a nice **big** house!" said the skunk.								
	Subtotal								
	Total								

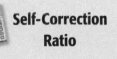

Accuracy Rate	**Errors**	14 or more	13	11–12	10	9	8	6–7	5	4	2–3	1	0
	%	Below 90%	90%	91%	92%	93%	94%	95%	96%	97%	98%	99%	100%

Self-Correction Ratio

(E + SC) ÷ SC = 1: _____

Fluency Score   0   1   2   3

Fluency Scoring Key

0 Reads primarily word-by-word with occasional but infrequent or inappropriate phrasing; no smooth or expressive interpretation, irregular pausing, and no attention to author's meaning or punctuation; no stress or inappropriate stress, and slow rate.

1 Reads primarily in two-word phrases with some three- and four-word groups and some word-by-word reading; almost no smooth, expressive interpretation or pausing guided by author's meaning and punctuation; almost no stress or inappropriate stress, with slow rate most of the time.

2 Reads primarily in three- or four-word phrase groups; some smooth, expressive interpretation and pausing guided by author's meaning and punctuation; mostly appropriate stress and rate with some slowdowns.

3 Reads primarily in larger, meaningful phrases or word groups; mostly smooth, expressive interpretation and pausing guided by author's meaning and punctuation; appropriate stress and rate with only a few slowdowns.

Part Two: Comprehension Conversation

Have a conversation with the student, noting the key understandings the student expresses. Use prompts as needed to stimulate discussion of understandings the student does not express. It is not necessary to use every prompt for each book. Score for evidence of all understandings expressed—with or without a prompt. Circle the number in the score column that reflects the level of understanding demonstrated.

Teacher: Talk about what happened in this story.

Comprehension Scoring Key	
0	Reflects **unsatisfactory** understanding of the text. Either does not respond or talks off the topic.
1	Reflects **limited** understanding of the text. Mentions a few facts or ideas but does not express the important information or ideas.
2	Reflects **satisfactory** understanding of the text. Includes important information and ideas but neglects other key understandings.
3	Reflects **excellent** understanding of the text. Includes almost all important information and main ideas.

Key Understandings	Prompts	Score
Within the Text All the animals went in the little house. The skunk went in the house and all the other animals came out (ran away). *Note any additional understandings:*	Talk about what happened first in this story. Then what happened? What happened at the end?	0 1 2 3
Beyond and About the Text The animals did not want to be in the house with the skunk because he might smell it up. The skunk felt good when he saw how big the house seemed when he was there by himself. The little house was big to the skunk because he was there all by himself (and/or he was little). The picture showed the skunk was happy (or had lots of room). *Note any additional understandings:*	Why did the animals run away? How do you think the skunk felt at the end of the story? Why? Why did the skunk call it a "nice big house" when all the other animals said it was a "nice little house"? Look at the last page. How do you know that the skunk really liked the little house?	0 1 2 3

Guide to Total Score

6–7 Excellent Comprehension

5   Satisfactory Comprehension

4   Limited Comprehension

0–3 Unsatisfactory Comprehension

Subtotal Score: _____ /6

Add 1 for any additional understandings: _____ /1

Total Score: _____ /7

Part Three: Writing About Reading *(optional)*

Read the writing/drawing prompt below to the student. You can also cut the prompt on the dotted line and give it to the child. Specify the amount of time for the student to complete the task on a separate sheet of paper. (See *Assessment Guide* for more information.)

Writing About Reading Scoring Key
0 Reflects **no** understanding of the text.
1 Reflects **very limited** understanding of the text.
2 Reflects **partial** understanding of the text.
3 Reflects **excellent** understanding of the text.

Write about what happened to the animals in the nice little house. You can draw a picture to go with your writing.

Student _____   Grade _____   Date _____

Teacher _____   School _____

Recording Form
Part One: Oral Reading

Place the book in front of the student. Read the title and introduction.

Introduction: Carl has a teacher named Mr. Brown. Carl tells all the things he and the other children in his class like to do with their teacher, Mr. Brown.

Summary of Scores:
Accuracy _____
Self-correction _____
Fluency _____
Comprehension _____
Writing _____

Sources of Information Used

Page	Text *Our Teacher Mr. Brown* Level D, RW: 113, E: 12	E	SC	E M	E S	E V	SC M	SC S	SC V
2	My name is Carl. I go to school. I like school. This is my teacher. My teacher's name is Mr. Brown.								
4	Mr. Brown reads books to us. We like the books.								
6	Mr. Brown helps us write stories. We like to write stories.								
	Subtotal								

© 2011, 2008 by Irene C. Fountas and Gay Su Pinnell. Portsmouth, NH: Heinemann. This page may be photocopied.

Part One: Oral Reading *continued*

Sources of Information Used

Page	Text	E	SC	E			SC		
				M	S	V	M	S	V
6 *cont.*	We like to read the stories to him.								
8	Mr. Brown helps us read books. We like to read books to him.								
10	We like to paint pictures. We like to draw pictures. Mr. Brown helps us.								
12	Mr. Brown plays games with us. We like to play ball.								
14	We like our school. We like to read books.								
	Subtotal								

Part One: Oral Reading *continued*

Sources of Information Used

Page	Text	E	SC	E			SC		
				M	S	V	M	S	V
15	We like to write stories. We like to play ball.								
16	We like our teacher, Mr. Brown!								
	Subtotal								
	Total								

Accuracy Rate	**Errors**	12 or more	11	10	9	8	7	6	4–5	3	2	1	0
	%	Below 90%	90%	91%	92%	93%	94%	95%	96%	97%	98%	99%	100%

Self-Correction Ratio

$(E + SC) \div SC = 1:$ ____

Fluency Score   0   1   2   3

Fluency Scoring Key

0 Reads primarily word-by-word with occasional but infrequent or inappropriate phrasing; no smooth or expressive interpretation, irregular pausing, and no attention to author's meaning or punctuation; no stress or inappropriate stress, and slow rate.

1 Reads primarily in two-word phrases with some three- and four-word groups and some word-by-word reading; almost no smooth, expressive interpretation or pausing guided by author's meaning and punctuation; almost no stress or inappropriate stress, with slow rate most of the time.

2 Reads primarily in three- or four-word phrase groups; some smooth, expressive interpretation and pausing guided by author's meaning and punctuation; mostly appropriate stress and rate with some slowdowns.

3 Reads primarily in larger, meaningful phrases or word groups; mostly smooth, expressive interpretation and pausing guided by author's meaning and punctuation; appropriate stress and rate with only a few slowdowns.

Part Two: Comprehension Conversation

Have a conversation with the student, noting the key understandings the student expresses. Use prompts as needed to stimulate discussion of understandings the student does not express. It is not necessary to use every prompt for each book. Score for evidence of all understandings expressed—with or without a prompt. Circle the number in the score column that reflects the level of understanding demonstrated.

Teacher: Talk about what you learned in this book.

Key Understandings	Prompts	Score
Within the Text Carl likes everything he does at school with his teacher. (Gives 2–3 examples, such as read books, write stories, listen to stories, paint pictures, and play ball.) Mr. Brown helps Carl and the other children do things at school. *Note any additional understandings:*	Carl and the other children like a lot of things they do with their teacher at school, don't they? What were some of those things? What does Mr. Brown do in this story?	0 1 2 3
Beyond and About the Text Carl likes school because he likes to (gives 1–2 examples, such as read books, write stories, listen to stories, paint pictures, play ball). I think Carl's favorite thing at school is (gives an example) because (any plausible reason). Mr. Brown is a good teacher because (any plausible reason). They do some things like we do at school, such as (gives 1–2 examples). *Note any additional understandings:*	Why do you think Carl likes school? What does Carl like most about school? Why do you think he likes that? What do you think about Mr. Brown? Was he a good teacher? Why? Did this story remind you of your teacher or class? Why?	0 1 2 3

Guide to Total Score

6–7 **Excellent** Comprehension

5 **Satisfactory** Comprehension

4 **Limited** Comprehension

0–3 **Unsatisfactory** Comprehension

Subtotal Score: _____ /6

Add 1 for any additional understandings: _____ /1

Total Score: _____ /7

Part Three: Writing About Reading *(optional)*

Read the writing/drawing prompt below to the student. You can also cut the prompt on the dotted line and give it to the child. Specify the amount of time for the student to complete the task on a separate sheet of paper. (See *Assessment Guide* for more information.)

Write about three things Mr. Brown helps the children do at school. You can draw a picture to go with your writing.

Student _____   Grade _____   Date _____

Teacher _____   School _____

Recording Form

Part One: Oral Reading

Place the book in front of the student. Read the title and introduction.

Summary of Scores:	
Accuracy	_____
Self-correction	_____
Fluency	_____
Comprehension	_____
Writing	_____

Introduction: Kate had a loose tooth and she tried lots of things to make it come out. Read to find out what happened to Kate's loose tooth.

Sources of Information Used

Page	Text *The Loose Tooth* Level E, RW: 198, E: 21	E	SC	E M	E S	E V	SC M	SC S	SC V
2	Kate had a loose tooth. Her tooth was **very** loose. Kate played with her tooth. But it did not come out.								
4	"Don't play with your tooth," said Kate's mom. "Eat your breakfast." "I want my tooth to come out," said Kate.								
	Subtotal								

Part One: Oral Reading *continued*

Sources of Information Used

Page	Text	E	SC	E			SC		
				M	S	V	M	S	V
5	"Your tooth will fall out," said Mom. Kate wiggled her tooth. But it did not fall out.								
6	Kate brushed her teeth after breakfast. She wanted her tooth to come out. She wanted it to come out **now**.								
7	She brushed and brushed. She brushed her loose tooth. But it did not fall out.								
	Subtotal								

Part One: Oral Reading *continued*

Sources of Information Used

Page	Text	E	SC	E			SC		
				M	S	V	M	S	V
8	Kate went to school. She played with her tooth at school.								
9	"Don't play with your tooth," said Kate's teacher.								
10	Kate played with her tooth at lunch. She wiggled it and wiggled it.								
11	"Don't wiggle your tooth," said Ben. "I want to eat my lunch."								
	Subtotal								

Part One: Oral Reading *continued*

Sources of Information Used

Page	Text	E	SC	E			SC		
				M	S	V	M	S	V
12	Kate went home. Her brother played with his blocks. Kate played with her tooth.								
13	"It is time to eat," said Mom. "Come and have some soup."								
14	Kate had some soup. She said, "Now I want an apple. I want a big, big apple."								
	Subtotal								

Part One: Oral Reading *continued*

Sources of Information Used

Page	Text	E	SC	E			SC		
				M	S	V	M	S	V
15	Kate took a big, big bite of her apple.								
16	"Look, Mom!" Kate said. "Look at my tooth **now**!"								
	Subtotal								
	Total								

Accuracy Rate	Errors	21 or more	19–20	17–18	15–16	13–14	11–12	9–10	7–8	5–6	3–4	1–2	0
	%	Below 90%	90%	91%	92%	93%	94%	95%	96%	97%	98%	99%	100%

Self-Correction Ratio

(E + SC) ÷ SC = 1: ____

Fluency Score   0   1   2   3

Fluency Scoring Key

0   Reads primarily word-by-word with occasional but infrequent or inappropriate phrasing; no smooth or expressive interpretation, irregular pausing, and no attention to author's meaning or punctuation; no stress or inappropriate stress, and slow rate.

1   Reads primarily in two-word phrases with some three- and four-word groups and some word-by-word reading; almost no smooth, expressive interpretation or pausing guided by author's meaning and punctuation; almost no stress or inappropriate stress, with slow rate most of the time.

2   Reads primarily in three- or four-word phrase groups; some smooth, expressive interpretation and pausing guided by author's meaning and punctuation; mostly appropriate stress and rate with some slowdowns.

3   Reads primarily in larger, meaningful phrases or word groups; mostly smooth, expressive interpretation and pausing guided by author's meaning and punctuation; appropriate stress and rate with only a few slowdowns.

Part Two: Comprehension Conversation

Have a conversation with the student, noting the key understandings the student expresses. Use prompts as needed to stimulate discussion of understandings the student does not express. It is not necessary to use every prompt for each book. Score for evidence of all understandings expressed—with or without a prompt. Circle the number in the score column that reflects the level of understanding demonstrated.

<table>
<tr><td colspan="2">**Comprehension Scoring Key**</td></tr>
<tr><td>**0**</td><td>Reflects **unsatisfactory** understanding of the text. Either does not respond or talks off the topic.</td></tr>
<tr><td>**1**</td><td>Reflects **limited** understanding of the text. Mentions a few facts or ideas but does not express the important information or ideas.</td></tr>
<tr><td>**2**</td><td>Reflects **satisfactory** understanding of the text. Includes important information and ideas but neglects other key understandings.</td></tr>
<tr><td>**3**</td><td>Reflects **excellent** understanding of the text. Includes almost all important information and main ideas.</td></tr>
</table>

Teacher: Talk about what happened in this story.

Key Understandings	Prompts	Score
Within the Text Kate had a loose tooth and she was doing everything she could to make it come out. (Gives 2–3 examples, such as wiggled it, played with it, brushed it.) In the end, she ate an apple and the tooth came out in her soup! *Note any additional understandings:*	What was Kate's problem in the story? What did Kate try to do to solve the problem? What else did she do? Talk about how the story ended.	0 1 2 3
Beyond and About the Text Kate really wanted her tooth to come out because (gives a plausible reason). She felt great when her tooth finally came out. Kate's mom wasn't worried because she knew the tooth would come out. The most important part of the story was when she took a bite of apple (or when the tooth fell out). *Note any additional understandings:*	Why do you think Kate really wanted her tooth to come out? Talk about how Kate felt about her tooth at the beginning of the story and at the end of the story. What do you think Kate's mom was thinking? What was the most important part of this story? Why?	0 1 2 3

Guide to Total Score

6–7 Excellent Comprehension

5   Satisfactory Comprehension

4   Limited Comprehension

0–3 Unsatisfactory Comprehension

Subtotal Score: _____ /6

Add 1 for any additional understandings: _____ /1

Total Score: _____ /7

Part Three: Writing About Reading *(optional)*

Read the writing/drawing prompt below to the student. You can also cut the prompt on the dotted line and give it to the child. Specify the amount of time for the student to complete the task on a separate sheet of paper. (See *Assessment Guide* for more information.)

<table>
<tr><td colspan="2">**Writing About Reading Scoring Key**</td></tr>
<tr><td>**0**</td><td>Reflects **no** understanding of the text.</td></tr>
<tr><td>**1**</td><td>Reflects **very limited** understanding of the text.</td></tr>
<tr><td>**2**</td><td>Reflects **partial** understanding of the text.</td></tr>
<tr><td>**3**</td><td>Reflects **excellent** understanding of the text.</td></tr>
</table>

Write about the three things Kate did to get her tooth to come out. You can draw a picture to go with your writing.

Recording Forms

Student _____   Grade _____   Date _____

Teacher _____   School _____

Recording Form
Part One: Oral Reading

Place the book in front of the student. Read the title and introduction.

Introduction: In this book, the author tells about all the animals you can see at the zoo.
Read to find out about the animals you can see.

	Summary of Scores:	
	Accuracy	_____
	Self-correction	_____
	Fluency	_____
	Comprehension	_____
	Writing	_____

Sources of Information Used

Page	Text *The Zoo* Level E, RW: 137, E: 15	E	SC	E			SC		
				M	S	V	M	S	V
2	You can see elephants at the zoo. The baby elephant can walk on the day it is born!								
4	You can see brown bears at the zoo. The baby bears stay with their mother.								
6	You can see polar bears at the zoo. Their fur is white. The fur keeps them warm.								
8	You can see lions at the zoo.								
	Subtotal								

Part One: Oral Reading *continued*

Sources of Information Used

Page	Text	E	SC	E			SC		
				M	S	V	M	S	V
8 *cont.*	The lions are resting. Lions rest for a long time every day.								
10	You can see giraffes at the zoo. Giraffes are tall animals. They can eat leaves from the tops of trees.								
12	You can see penguins at the zoo. These birds can not fly. But they can swim!								
14	You can see chimps at the zoo. The chimps like to climb trees. They hold on to the trees with their big hands.								
	Subtotal								

Part One: Oral Reading *continued*

Sources of Information Used

Page	Text	E	SC	E			SC		
				M	S	V	M	S	V
16	You can see all the animals at the zoo!								
	Subtotal								
	Total								

Accuracy Rate	**Errors**	15 or more	14	12–13	11	9–10	8	7	5–6	4	3	1–2	0
	%	Below 90%	90%	91%	92%	93%	94%	95%	96%	97%	98%	99%	100%

Self-Correction Ratio	(E + SC) ÷ SC = 1: _____

Fluency Score	0 1 2 3

Fluency Scoring Key

0   Reads primarily word-by-word with occasional but infrequent or inappropriate phrasing; no smooth or expressive interpretation, irregular pausing, and no attention to author's meaning or punctuation; no stress or inappropriate stress, and slow rate.

1   Reads primarily in two-word phrases with some three- and four-word groups and some word-by-word reading; almost no smooth, expressive interpretation or pausing guided by author's meaning and punctuation; almost no stress or inappropriate stress, with slow rate most of the time.

2   Reads primarily in three- or four-word phrase groups; some smooth, expressive interpretation and pausing guided by author's meaning and punctuation; mostly appropriate stress and rate with some slowdowns.

3   Reads primarily in larger, meaningful phrases or word groups; mostly smooth, expressive interpretation and pausing guided by author's meaning and punctuation; appropriate stress and rate with only a few slowdowns.

Part Two: Comprehension Conversation

Have a conversation with the student, noting the key understandings the student expresses. Use prompts as needed to stimulate discussion of understandings the student does not express. It is not necessary to use every prompt for each book. Score for evidence of all understandings expressed—with or without a prompt. Circle the number in the score column that reflects the level of understanding demonstrated.

<table>
<tr><td colspan="2">**Comprehension Scoring Key**</td></tr>
<tr><td>**0**</td><td>Reflects **unsatisfactory** understanding of the text. Either does not respond or talks off the topic.</td></tr>
<tr><td>**1**</td><td>Reflects **limited** understanding of the text. Mentions a few facts or ideas but does not express the important information or ideas.</td></tr>
<tr><td>**2**</td><td>Reflects **satisfactory** understanding of the text. Includes important information and ideas but neglects other key understandings.</td></tr>
<tr><td>**3**</td><td>Reflects **excellent** understanding of the text. Includes almost all important information and main ideas.</td></tr>
</table>

Teacher: Talk about what you learned in this book.

Key Understandings	Prompts	Score
Within the Text You can see lots of animals at the zoo. (Gives 2–3 examples such as chimps, elephants, giraffes, penguins, polar bears, lions, and brown bears.) Accept a variety of facts about the book such as: lions resting for a long time; chimps liking to climb trees; baby elephants walking on the day they are born; giraffes eating leaves; penguins swimming; polar bears having thick, white fur; baby bears staying with their mother. *Note any additional understandings:*	What are some of the animals you can see at the zoo? What did you learn about the animals at the zoo? What else did you learn?	0 1 2 3
Beyond and About the Text The zoo is a fun place to go because you can see animals and learn about them. This book helps you know what a zoo is like so you may want to go there (or other plausible reason). The author shows photographs and tells information about the animals. *Note any additional understandings:*	Why do people like to go to the zoo? Why do you think this author wanted to tell you about animals you can see at the zoo? How does the author help you learn about animals at the zoo?	0 1 2 3

Guide to Total Score

6–7 **Excellent** Comprehension

5   **Satisfactory** Comprehension

4   **Limited** Comprehension

0–3 **Unsatisfactory** Comprehension

Subtotal Score: _____ /6

Add 1 for any additional understandings: _____ /1

Total Score: _____ /7

Part Three: Writing About Reading *(optional)*

Read the writing/drawing prompt below to the student. You can also cut the prompt on the dotted line and give it to the child. Specify the amount of time for the student to complete the task on a separate sheet of paper. (See *Assessment Guide* for more information.)

<table>
<tr><td colspan="2">**Writing About Reading Scoring Key**</td></tr>
<tr><td>**0**</td><td>Reflects **no** understanding of the text.</td></tr>
<tr><td>**1**</td><td>Reflects **very limited** understanding of the text.</td></tr>
<tr><td>**2**</td><td>Reflects **partial** understanding of the text.</td></tr>
<tr><td>**3**</td><td>Reflects **excellent** understanding of the text.</td></tr>
</table>

Write about three things you learned about the animals at the zoo.

You can draw a picture to go with your writing.

Student _____   Grade _____   Date _____

Teacher _____   School _____

Recording Form

Part One: Oral Reading

Place the book in front of the student. Read the title and introduction.

Introduction: Anna was getting ready for school. Her mom said she might need to get glasses to see better. But Anna didn't want glasses. Read to find out what happened when she got her new glasses.

Summary of Scores:	
Accuracy	_____
Self-correction	_____
Fluency	_____
Comprehension	_____
Writing	_____

Sources of Information Used

Page	Text *Anna's New Glasses* Level F, RW: 220, E: 24	E	SC	E			SC		
				M	S	V	M	S	V
2	"I am ready for school," said Anna. She had a new red backpack and new shoes. "We have one more thing to do," said her mom. "You may need to get some glasses."								
4	"I **don't** need glasses!" said Anna. "You may need glasses to help you read," said her mom. "Do you want to read at school?"								
	Subtotal								

Part One: Oral Reading *continued*

Sources of Information Used

Page	Text	E	SC	E			SC		
				M	S	V	M	S	V
5	"I want to read," said Anna. "I love books! But I don't want glasses."								
6	Anna went to the doctor. "You **do** need glasses," said the doctor.								
7	Anna looked at the glasses.								
8	"I don't like these glasses," she said.								
9	"Look at the purple glasses," said Mom. Anna put on the purple glasses.								
	Subtotal								

Part One: Oral Reading *continued*

Sources of Information Used

Page	Text	E	SC	E			SC		
				M	S	V	M	S	V
11	Anna put on some red glasses. "I like red and I like these red glasses," she said. "You look great in those glasses," said Mom.								
12	It was the first day of school. Anna put her new red glasses in her new red backpack.								
13	"Don't forget your glasses," said Mom. "I put them in my backpack," said Anna.								
	Subtotal								

Part One: Oral Reading *continued*

Sources of Information Used

Page	Text	E	SC	E			SC		
				M	S	V	M	S	V
13 *cont.*	"Put your glasses on at school," said Mom.								
15	Anna and her mom walked to school. Anna looked at her new teacher. She opened her backpack and put on her new glasses.								
16	"I am Mrs. Bell," the teacher said. "I am your new teacher. We have the same glasses!" Anna smiled. "Yes, these are **great** glasses!"								
	Subtotal								

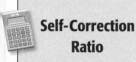

Accuracy Rate	Errors	24 or more	21–23	19–20	17–18	15–16	13–14	10–12	8–9	6–7	4–5	1–3	0
	%	Below 90%	90%	91%	92%	93%	94%	95%	96%	97%	98%	99%	100%

Self-Correction Ratio	(E + SC) ÷ SC = 1: _____

Fluency Score	0 1 2 3	

Fluency Scoring Key

0 Reads primarily word-by-word with occasional but infrequent or inappropriate phrasing; no smooth or expressive interpretation, irregular pausing, and no attention to author's meaning or punctuation; no stress or inappropriate stress, and slow rate.

1 Reads primarily in two-word phrases with some three- and four-word groups and some word-by-word reading; almost no smooth, expressive interpretation or pausing guided by author's meaning and punctuation; almost no stress or inappropriate stress, with slow rate most of the time.

2 Reads primarily in three- or four-word phrase groups; some smooth, expressive interpretation and pausing guided by author's meaning and punctuation; mostly appropriate stress and rate with some slowdowns.

3 Reads primarily in larger, meaningful phrases or word groups; mostly smooth, expressive interpretation and pausing guided by author's meaning and punctuation; appropriate stress and rate with only a few slowdowns.

Part Two: Comprehension Conversation

Have a conversation with the student, noting the key understandings the student expresses. Use prompts as needed to stimulate discussion of understandings the student does not express. It is not necessary to use every prompt for each book. Score for evidence of all understandings expressed—with or without a prompt. Circle the number in the score column that reflects the level of understanding demonstrated.

Teacher: Talk about what happened in this story.

Key Understandings	Prompts	Score
Within the Text Anna had to get glasses to see better but she did not want to wear them. Recounts the major events of the story, such as: Anna didn't want to get new glasses; she tried on many different glasses and chose red ones; she got some new glasses but she didn't want to wear them; she put them on when she saw that her teacher's glasses were the same as hers. *Note any additional understandings:*	What was Anna's problem in this story? What happened in this story? Then what happened? What happened at the end of the story?	0 1 2 3
Beyond and About the Text Anna didn't want to wear glasses to school because (any plausible explanation). Anna felt good when she saw her teacher had glasses just like hers. Anna felt good because she would not look so different from everyone else. The pictures showed the teacher with her glasses, so I knew Anna would put hers on. *Note any additional understandings:*	Talk about how Anna felt at the beginning of the story. How did Anna feel about wearing glasses when she got to school? Why? Talk about how Anna felt at the end of the story. Why? Look at the picture on page 14. How can you predict that Anna will put on her glasses?	0 1 2 3

Guide to Total Score

6–7 **Excellent** Comprehension

5   **Satisfactory** Comprehension

4   **Limited** Comprehension

0–3 **Unsatisfactory** Comprehension

Subtotal Score: _____ /6

Add 1 for any additional understandings: _____ /1

Total Score: _____ /7

Part Three: Writing About Reading *(optional)*

Read the writing/drawing prompt below to the student. You can also cut the prompt on the dotted line and give it to the child. Specify the amount of time for the student to complete the task on a separate sheet of paper. (See *Assessment Guide* for more information.)

Write about how Anna felt about her new glasses. You can draw a picture to go with your writing.

Student _____   Grade _____   Date _____

Teacher _____   School _____

Recording Form

Part One: Oral Reading

Place the book in front of the student. Read the title and introduction.

Introduction: Mother Bird makes a nest with sticks and grass and then she lays her eggs in the nest. Read to find out what she does to take care of her new baby birds.

Summary of Scores:	
Accuracy	_____
Self-correction	_____
Fluency	_____
Comprehension	_____
Writing	_____

Sources of Information Used

Page	Text *From Nest to Bird* Level F, RW: 165, E: 18	E	SC	E			SC		
				M	S	V	M	S	V
2	This is Mother Bird. What does Mother Bird do?								
3	Mother Bird gets sticks and grass. She makes a nest.								
4	Why does Mother Bird need a nest?								
5	Mother Bird needs a nest for her eggs! She lays eggs in the nest. The eggs are blue.								
	Subtotal								

Part One: Oral Reading *continued*

Sources of Information Used

Page	Text	E	SC	E			SC		
				M	S	V	M	S	V
6	What does Mother Bird do now?								
7	Mother Bird sits on the eggs. She keeps the eggs warm.								
8	Why does Mother Bird keep the eggs warm?								
9	Baby birds are in the eggs. The baby birds will come out of the eggs soon!								
10	The baby birds are out! What does Mother Bird do now?								
	Subtotal								

Part One: Oral Reading *continued*

Sources of Information Used

Page	Text	E	SC	E M	E S	E V	SC M	SC S	SC V
11	Mother Bird feeds her baby birds. She feeds bugs to them.								
12	The baby birds chirp and chirp. They want to eat more bugs. Where is Mother Bird?								
13	Mother Bird gets more bugs. The baby birds eat and eat.								
14	The baby birds hop up and down. Why do they hop?								
	Subtotal								

Part One: Oral Reading *continued*

Sources of Information Used

Page	Text	E	SC	E			SC		
				M	S	V	M	S	V
15	The baby birds hop and hop. Soon they will fly!								
16	Look at the baby birds! The baby birds can fly!								
	Subtotal								
	Total								

Accuracy Rate	**Errors**	18 or more	16–17	15	13–14	11–12	10	8–9	6–7	5	3–4	1–2	0
	%	Below 90%	90%	91%	92%	93%	94%	95%	96%	97%	98%	99%	100%

Self-Correction Ratio	(E + SC) ÷ SC = 1: _____

Fluency Score   0   1   2   3

Fluency Scoring Key

0 Reads primarily word-by-word with occasional but infrequent or inappropriate phrasing; no smooth or expressive interpretation, irregular pausing, and no attention to author's meaning or punctuation; no stress or inappropriate stress, and slow rate.

1 Reads primarily in two-word phrases with some three- and four-word groups and some word-by-word reading; almost no smooth, expressive interpretation or pausing guided by author's meaning and punctuation; almost no stress or inappropriate stress, with slow rate most of the time.

2 Reads primarily in three- or four-word phrase groups; some smooth, expressive interpretation and pausing guided by author's meaning and punctuation; mostly appropriate stress and rate with some slowdowns.

3 Reads primarily in larger, meaningful phrases or word groups; mostly smooth, expressive interpretation and pausing guided by author's meaning and punctuation; appropriate stress and rate with only a few slowdowns.

Part Two: Comprehension Conversation

Have a conversation with the student, noting the key understandings the student expresses. Use prompts as needed to stimulate discussion of understandings the student does not express. It is not necessary to use every prompt for each book. Score for evidence of all understandings expressed—with or without a prompt. Circle the number in the score column that reflects the level of understanding demonstrated.

Teacher: Talk about what you learned in this book.

Comprehension Scoring Key
0 Reflects **unsatisfactory** understanding of the text. Either does not respond or talks off the topic.
1 Reflects **limited** understanding of the text. Mentions a few facts or ideas but does not express the important information or ideas.
2 Reflects **satisfactory** understanding of the text. Includes important information and ideas but neglects other key understandings.
3 Reflects **excellent** understanding of the text. Includes almost all important information and main ideas.

Key Understandings	Prompts	Score
Within the Text Recounts most of the events in order such as: Mother Bird makes a nest with sticks and grass; she lays eggs; she sits on the eggs; baby birds hatch; she feeds bugs to the baby birds; baby birds hop; baby birds fly. *Note any additional understandings:*	What happened first in the book? What happened next? What happened at the end?	0 1 2 3
Beyond and About the Text The eggs have to stay warm so that the little birds inside can (stay alive, grow). Mother Bird needs to do these things because baby birds are helpless and must be taken care of. Baby birds have to peck themselves out of the eggs when they are big enough; they can't fly right after they hatch. They have to learn. In this book, the author always asks a question and then gives an answer. Some of the questions you have to think about. *Note any additional understandings:*	Why does Mother Bird have to sit on the nest? Why does Mother Bird have to do things for the baby birds? What are some of the things the baby birds have to do for themselves? Look at page 14. What question is the author asking? Does the author answer the question? (No, but it is implied.) What do you think is the answer?	0 1 2 3

Guide to Total Score
6–7 Excellent Comprehension
5 Satisfactory Comprehension
4 Limited Comprehension
0–3 Unsatisfactory Comprehension

Subtotal Score: _____ /6

Add 1 for any additional understandings: _____ /1

Total Score: _____ /7

Part Three: Writing About Reading *(optional)*

Read the writing/drawing prompt below to the student. You can also cut the prompt on the dotted line and give it to the child. Specify the amount of time for the student to complete the task on a separate sheet of paper. (See *Assessment Guide* for more information.)

Writing About Reading Scoring Key
0 Reflects **no** understanding of the text.
1 Reflects **very limited** understanding of the text.
2 Reflects **partial** understanding of the text.
3 Reflects **excellent** understanding of the text.

Write about how Mother Bird took care of her eggs and her baby birds. You can draw a picture to go with your writing.

Recording Forms

Student _____   Grade _____   Date _____

Teacher _____   School _____

Recording Form
Part One: Oral Reading

Place the book in front of the student. Read the title and introduction.

Introduction: Nick went to bed but something was missing, and he could not go to sleep.
Read to find out how his mom helped him find what was missing.

Summary of Scores:	
Accuracy	_____
Self-correction	_____
Fluency	_____
Comprehension	_____
Writing	_____

Sources of Information Used

Page	Text *Bedtime for Nick* Level G, RW: 216, E: 23	E	SC	E			SC		
				M	S	V	M	S	V
2	Nick was looking at his book. His mom came in and said, "It's time for bed." "Okay, Mom," said Nick.								
4	Nick put on his pajamas. He washed his face and brushed his teeth. He was ready for bed.								
5	Nick got into his bed.								
	Subtotal								

Part One: Oral Reading *continued*

Sources of Information Used

Page	Text	E	SC	E			SC		
				M	S	V	M	S	V
6	"Will you read me a story?" Nick asked his mom. Mom read the story to Nick. Nick liked the story about the magic fish. When the story was over, Nick's mom turned off the light.								
7	"Good night, Nick," his mom said.								
8	"Will you turn on the nightlight?" asked Nick. "Okay, Nick," his mom said. She turned it on.								
	Subtotal								

Part One: Oral Reading *continued*

© 2011, 2008 by Irene C. Fountas and Gay Su Pinnell. Portsmouth, NH: Heinemann. This page may be photocopied.

Sources of Information Used

Page	Text	E	SC	E			SC		
				M	S	V	M	S	V
9	"Good night, Nick," his mom said. "Now it's time to go to sleep."								
10	"I can't go to sleep," said Nick. "I will give you a good night kiss," said Nick's mom.								
11	"Good night, Nick," his mom said. "Go to sleep now."								
12	"I **can't** go to sleep," said Nick. "Will you open the door?" he asked. Nick's mom opened the door. Light came into the room.								
	Subtotal								

Part One: Oral Reading *continued*

Page	Text	E	SC	Sources of Information Used					
				E			**SC**		
				M	S	V	M	S	V
13	"Good night, Nick," his mom said.								
14	"I **can't** go to sleep," said Nick. "Something is missing." He looked around the room. Something came in the door.								
15	"Wags! You're late," said Nick. "Now **we** can go to sleep."								
16	"Good night, Nick," said Mom. "Good night, Wags." "Good night, Mom," said Nick.								
	Subtotal								
	Total								

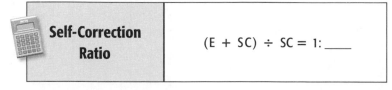

Accuracy Rate	Errors	23 or more	21–22	19–20	17–18	15–16	12–14	10–11	8–9	6–7	4–5	1–3	0
	%	Below 90%	90%	91%	92%	93%	94%	95%	96%	97%	98%	99%	100%

Self-Correction Ratio	
	(E + SC) ÷ SC = 1: _____

Fluency Score	0 1 2 3	**Fluency Scoring Key**

Fluency Scoring Key

0 Reads primarily word-by-word with occasional but infrequent or inappropriate phrasing; no smooth or expressive interpretation, irregular pausing, and no attention to author's meaning or punctuation; no stress or inappropriate stress, and slow rate.

1 Reads primarily in two-word phrases with some three- and four-word groups and some word-by-word reading; almost no smooth, expressive interpretation or pausing guided by author's meaning and punctuation; almost no stress or inappropriate stress, with slow rate most of the time.

2 Reads primarily in three- or four-word phrase groups; some smooth, expressive interpretation and pausing guided by author's meaning and punctuation; mostly appropriate stress and rate with some slowdowns.

3 Reads primarily in larger, meaningful phrases or word groups; mostly smooth, expressive interpretation and pausing guided by author's meaning and punctuation; appropriate stress and rate with only a few slowdowns.

© 2011, 2008 by Irene C. Fountas and Gay Su Pinnell. Portsmouth, NH: Heinemann. This page may be photocopied.

Part Two: Comprehension Conversation

Have a conversation with the student, noting the key understandings the student expresses. Use prompts as needed to stimulate discussion of understandings the student does not express. It is not necessary to use every prompt for each book. Score for evidence of all understandings expressed—with or without a prompt. Circle the number in the score column that reflects the level of understanding demonstrated.

Teacher: Talk about what happened in this story.

Comprehension Scoring Key
0   Reflects **unsatisfactory** understanding of the text. Either does not respond or talks off the topic.
1   Reflects **limited** understanding of the text. Mentions a few facts or ideas but does not express the important information or ideas.
2   Reflects **satisfactory** understanding of the text. Includes important information and ideas but neglects other key understandings.
3   Reflects **excellent** understanding of the text. Includes almost all important information and main ideas.

Key Understandings	Prompts	Score
Within the Text Nick got ready for bed. He went to bed but he couldn't go to sleep. He told his mom to do different things to help him. (Gives 2–3 examples, such as read a story; turn on the nightlight; give a kiss; open the door.) His dog (Wags) came in and then he went to sleep. *Note any additional understandings:*	What happened in this story? What did Nick ask his mom to do to help him sleep? What else did she do? How did the story end?	0 1 2 3
Beyond and About the Text Nick didn't know why he couldn't sleep. (Or, he really did know.) Nick missed Wags and that's why he couldn't go to sleep. Wags might have been taking a walk with Dad (or any plausible reason). The most important part of the story was when you see Wags' tail in the picture. Nick loves Wags and that's why he missed him and couldn't sleep. *Note any additional understandings:*	Do you think Nick really knew why he couldn't sleep? What makes you think that? What was the real reason that Nick couldn't go to sleep? I wonder why Wags was so late going to bed. What do you think? Show me the most important part of the story. How do you think Nick feels about Wags?	0 1 2 3

Guide to Total Score
6–7 Excellent Comprehension
5   **Satisfactory** Comprehension
4   **Limited** Comprehension
0–3 Unsatisfactory Comprehension

Subtotal Score: _____/6

Add 1 for any additional understandings: _____/1

Total Score: _____/7

Part Three: Writing About Reading *(optional)*

Read the writing/drawing prompt below to the student. You can also cut the prompt on the dotted line and give it to the child. Specify the amount of time for the student to complete the task on a separate sheet of paper. (See *Assessment Guide* for more information.)

Writing About Reading Scoring Key
0 Reflects **no** understanding of the text.
1 Reflects **very limited** understanding of the text.
2 Reflects **partial** understanding of the text.
3 Reflects **excellent** understanding of the text.

Write about Nick and what helped him go to sleep. You can draw a picture to go with your writing.

Recording Forms

Student _____   Grade _____   Date _____

Teacher _____   School _____

Recording Form
Part One: Oral Reading

Place the book in front of the student. Read the title and introduction.

Introduction: Bubbles are filled with air like balloons. Read to find out about all different kinds of bubbles and how they are made.

Summary of Scores:

Accuracy	_____
Self-correction	_____
Fluency	_____
Comprehension	_____
Writing	_____

Sources of Information Used

Page	Text *Bubbles* Level G, RW: 152, E: 16	E	SC	E M	E S	E V	SC M	SC S	SC V
2	Look at all the bubbles! Some bubbles are big and some are little.								
3	All these bubbles are made with soap and water. They are called soap bubbles.								
4	Soap bubbles are pretty. They are very shiny, and they have lots of colors, just like a rainbow.								
6	What is inside all the bubbles? Bubbles are like little balloons. They are filled with air.								
	Subtotal								

Part One: Oral Reading *continued*

Sources of Information Used

Page	Text	E	SC	E			SC		
				M	S	V	M	S	V
8	Little bubbles have a little air inside. Big ones have more air inside.								
9	This boy is blowing air to make a soap bubble.								
10	This girl is blowing air into a straw. The air is going into the girl's milk to make bubbles.								
12	Here is an enormous bubble. This bubble is as long as a van! It has lots of air inside.								
	Subtotal								

Part One: Oral Reading *continued*

Sources of Information Used

Page	Text	E	SC	E			SC		
				M	S	V	M	S	V
14	Don't forget about bubble gum! This boy is blowing air into his gum to make a big, big bubble. If he blows in too much air...								
16	...the bubble will **pop**!								
	Subtotal								
	Total								

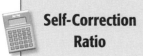

Accuracy Rate	Errors	16 or more	15	13–14	12	10–11	9	7–8	6	4–5	3	1–2	0
	%	Below 90%	90%	91%	92%	93%	94%	95%	96%	97%	98%	99%	100%

Self-Correction Ratio	(E + SC) ÷ SC = 1: ____

Fluency Score	0 1 2 3	**Fluency Scoring Key**

0 Reads primarily word-by-word with occasional but infrequent or inappropriate phrasing; no smooth or expressive interpretation, irregular pausing, and no attention to author's meaning or punctuation; no stress or inappropriate stress, and slow rate.

1 Reads primarily in two-word phrases with some three- and four-word groups and some word-by-word reading; almost no smooth, expressive interpretation or pausing guided by author's meaning and punctuation; almost no stress or inappropriate stress, with slow rate most of the time.

2 Reads primarily in three- or four-word phrase groups; some smooth, expressive interpretation and pausing guided by author's meaning and punctuation; mostly appropriate stress and rate with some slowdowns.

3 Reads primarily in larger, meaningful phrases or word groups; mostly smooth, expressive interpretation and pausing guided by author's meaning and punctuation; appropriate stress and rate with only a few slowdowns.

Recording Forms

Part Two: Comprehension Conversation

Have a conversation with the student, noting the key understandings the student expresses. Use prompts as needed to stimulate discussion of understandings the student does not express. It is not necessary to use every prompt for each book. Score for evidence of all understandings expressed—with or without a prompt. Circle the number in the score column that reflects the level of understanding demonstrated.

Teacher: Talk about what you learned in this book.

Comprehension Scoring Key

0   Reflects **unsatisfactory** understanding of the text. Either does not respond or talks off the topic.

1   Reflects **limited** understanding of the text. Mentions a few facts or ideas but does not express the important information or ideas.

2   Reflects **satisfactory** understanding of the text. Includes important information and ideas but neglects other key understandings.

3   Reflects **excellent** understanding of the text. Includes almost all important information and main ideas.

Key Understandings	Prompts	Score
Within the Text There are all kinds of bubbles. (Names 2–3 examples, such as soap bubbles, milk bubbles, or bubble gum.) Recounts 3–4 facts about bubbles from the book such as: can be made with soap and water; can have colors in them; are filled with air; can be made by blowing air; can be big or little; will pop if you blow in too much air. *Note any additional understandings:*	What are some kinds of bubbles? What did you learn about bubbles? What else did you learn about bubbles and how they are made?	0 1 2 3
Beyond and About the Text Bubbles get bigger when they have more air inside them. Bubbles are like balloons because they have air inside them. Bubbles can pop if they get too much air inside them. The book was funny when the boy blew the bubble and it popped on his face. *Note any additional understandings:*	How do bubbles get bigger? How are bubbles like balloons? Why do bubbles pop? What was the funny part of the book?	0 1 2 3

Guide to Total Score

6–7 Excellent Comprehension

5   **Satisfactory** Comprehension

4   **Limited** Comprehension

0–3 Unsatisfactory Comprehension

Subtotal Score: _____ /6

Add 1 for any additional understandings: _____ /1

Total Score: _____ /7

Part Three: Writing About Reading (optional)

Read the writing/drawing prompt on the next page to the student. Specify the amount of time for the student to complete the task. (See *Assessment Guide* for more information.)

Writing About Reading Scoring Key

0   Reflects **no** understanding of the text.

1   Reflects **very limited** understanding of the text.

2   Reflects **partial** understanding of the text.

3   Reflects **excellent** understanding of the text.

Write about three interesting things you learned about bubbles. You can draw a picture to go with your writing.

Student _____   Grade _____   Date _____

Teacher _____   School _____

Recording Form
Part One: Oral Reading

Place the book in front of the student. Read the title and introduction.

Introduction: Jim was invited to a sleepover party. He was worried about staying at his friend's house and wanted to take his favorite toy Mugsy with him. Read to find out what happened.

Summary of Scores:

Accuracy	_____
Self-correction	_____
Fluency	_____
Comprehension	_____
Writing	_____

Sources of Information Used

Page	Text *The Sleepover Party* Level H, RW: 288, E: 31	E	SC	E M	E S	E V	SC M	SC S	SC V
2	Jim was excited because he was going to a sleepover party! But he was also a little worried. He had never stayed all night at a friend's house.								
3	All of Jim's friends were invited to the party, too. Jim said, "See you at Matt's house!" But he was still worried.								
4	Mom helped Jim pack for the party. "Here are your pajamas and your toothbrush," said Mom.								
	Subtotal								

Part One: Oral Reading *continued*

Sources of Information Used

Page	Text	E	SC	E			SC		
				M	S	V	M	S	V
5	Jim wasn't really listening because he was worrying. "What if I miss Mom?" he thought. "What if I can't fall asleep?"								
6	Mom held up Jim's favorite toy. "Do you want to take Mugsy with you?" Mom asked. Jim always slept with Mugsy.								
7	Jim did want to bring Mugsy. But he was worried. "Mugsy is a baby toy," Jim told his mom. "I don't want my friends to laugh at me. I **can't** bring Mugsy."								
	Subtotal								

Part One: Oral Reading *continued*

Sources of Information Used

Page	Text	E	SC	E			SC		
				M	S	V	M	S	V
8	"That's fine," said Mom. "Get your sleeping bag. I'll zip up your backpack."								
9	"Have fun," Mom said. "I will," Jim answered. But he was still a little worried.								
10	All of Jim's friends were at Matt's house. They played games and they ate yummy snacks. Jim was having fun.								
11	Then it was time for bed. All the boys went up to Matt's room.								
	Subtotal								

Part One: Oral Reading *continued*

Sources of Information Used

Page	Text	E	SC	E M	E S	E V	SC M	SC S	SC V
12	Dan opened his backpack and pulled out a toy. "Here is Teddy!" said Dan. "I always sleep with him." Luis opened his backpack. "I have Snapper!" he said.								
13	Josh had a toy, too. "I always take Spot with me!" he said.								
14	"I wish I had Mugsy," Jim thought. Matt said, "Jim, are you going to get ready for bed?"								
15	"Sure," said Jim. He opened his backpack to look for his pajamas.								
	Subtotal								

Part One: Oral Reading *continued*

Sources of Information Used

Page	Text	E	SC	E			SC		
				M	S	V	M	S	V
16	"What's this?" said Jim. It was Mugsy! Mugsy came to the sleepover party after all!								
	Subtotal								
	Total								

Accuracy Rate	Errors	31 or more	28–30	25–27	22–24	19–21	16–18	13–15	11–12	8–10	5–7	1–4	0
	%	Below 90%	90%	91%	92%	93%	94%	95%	96%	97%	98%	99%	100%

Self-Correction Ratio

(E + SC) ÷ SC = 1: ____

Fluency Score   0   1   2   3

Fluency Scoring Key

0   Reads primarily word-by-word with occasional but infrequent or inappropriate phrasing; no smooth or expressive interpretation, irregular pausing, and no attention to author's meaning or punctuation; no stress or inappropriate stress, and slow rate.

1   Reads primarily in two-word phrases with some three- and four-word groups and some word-by-word reading; almost no smooth, expressive interpretation or pausing guided by author's meaning and punctuation; almost no stress or inappropriate stress, with slow rate most of the time.

2   Reads primarily in three- or four-word phrase groups; some smooth, expressive interpretation and pausing guided by author's meaning and punctuation; mostly appropriate stress and rate with some slowdowns.

3   Reads primarily in larger, meaningful phrases or word groups; mostly smooth, expressive interpretation and pausing guided by author's meaning and punctuation; appropriate stress and rate with only a few slowdowns.

Recording Forms

Part Two: Comprehension Conversation

Have a conversation with the student, noting the key understandings the student expresses. Use prompts as needed to stimulate discussion of understandings the student does not express. It is not necessary to use every prompt for each book. Score for evidence of all understandings expressed—with or without a prompt. Circle the number in the score column that reflects the level of understanding demonstrated.

Teacher: Talk about what happened in this story.

Comprehension Scoring Key

0   Reflects **unsatisfactory** understanding of the text. Either does not respond or talks off the topic.

1   Reflects **limited** understanding of the text. Mentions a few facts or ideas but does not express the important information or ideas.

2   Reflects **satisfactory** understanding of the text. Includes important information and ideas but neglects other key understandings.

3   Reflects **excellent** understanding of the text. Includes almost all important information and main ideas.

Key Understandings	Prompts	Score
Within the Text Jim was going to his first sleepover party and he didn't know whether to take his toy. Recounts most of the important events of the story in order, such as Jim went to a sleepover party; he didn't know whether to take Mugsy; all the other boys brought their toys; Jim missed Mugsy; Jim found Mugsy in his bag. *Note any additional understandings:*	What was the problem in the story? What happened in the story? Then what happened? What was the surprise at the end?	0 1 2 3
Beyond and About the Text Jim was worried about being away from home for the first time. Jim was worried that the other kids would make fun of him for bringing Mugsy. Mom put Mugsy in Jim's bag. Jim was glad to see Mugsy. The picture shows Mom putting Mugsy in Jim's backpack. *Note any additional understandings:*	Talk about how Jim felt about going to the sleepover party. Why was Jim worried about taking Mugsy to the party? How did Mugsy get in Jim's bag? Why do you think his mom did that? How did Jim feel at the end of the story? Show me the page where the picture helped you know how Mugsy got to the party.	0 1 2 3

Guide to Total Score

6–7 Excellent Comprehension

5   **Satisfactory** Comprehension

4   **Limited** Comprehension

0–3 Unsatisfactory Comprehension

Subtotal Score: _____ /6

Add 1 for any additional understandings: _____ /1

Total Score: _____ /7

Part Three: Writing About Reading *(optional)*

Read the writing/drawing prompt below to the student. You can also cut the prompt on the dotted line and give it to the child. Specify the amount of time for the student to complete the task on a separate sheet of paper. (See *Assessment Guide* for more information.)

Writing About Reading Scoring Key

0 Reflects **no** understanding of the text.

1 Reflects **very limited** understanding of the text.

2 Reflects **partial** understanding of the text.

3 Reflects **excellent** understanding of the text.

Write about how Jim felt about the sleepover party at the beginning of the story and how he felt at the end. You can draw a picture to go with your writing.

Student _____   Grade _____   Date _____

Teacher _____   School _____

Recording Form
Part One: Oral Reading

Summary of Scores:	
Accuracy	_____
Self-correction	_____
Fluency	_____
Comprehension	_____
Writing	_____

Place the book in front of the student. Read the title and introduction.

Introduction: There are many kinds of trucks and they do important jobs. Read to find out
about the different kinds of trucks and the jobs they do.

Sources of Information Used

Page	Text *Trucks* Level H, RW: 188, E: 20	E	SC	E M	E S	E V	SC M	SC S	SC V
2	Big trucks are on the road. They are going to many different places. They are going to do many important jobs.								
4	This is a fire truck. Fire trucks help put out fires. This truck has a long hose that shoots water on the fire.								
6	This truck picks up trash. The trash goes in the back of the truck. The truck crushes the trash to make it smaller. Then the truck carries the trash away.								
	Subtotal								

Part One: Oral Reading *continued*

Sources of Information Used

Page	Text	E	SC	E			SC		
				M	S	V	M	S	V
8	This is a mail truck. It picks up mail from the post office. Then the truck carries the mail all over town.								
10	This big truck is a snowplow. It pushes the snow to the side of the road. Then big trucks come to carry the piles of snow away.								
12	This truck carries all kinds of food. The truck picks up corn at the farm. Then it takes the corn to the market.								
14	This is an ice cream truck. The ice cream truck plays a song.								
	Subtotal								

Part One: Oral Reading *continued*

Sources of Information Used

Page	Text	E	SC	E			SC		
				M	S	V	M	S	V
14 *cont.*	Children hear the song and run to get ice cream.								
16	All kinds of trucks are on the road. Some trucks are for work. And some trucks are for play.								
	Subtotal								
	Total								

Accuracy Rate

Errors	20 or more	18–19	16–17	15	13–14	11–12	9–10	7–8	5–6	3–4	1–2	0
%	Below 90%	90%	91%	92%	93%	94%	95%	96%	97%	98%	99%	100%

Self-Correction Ratio

(E + SC) ÷ SC = 1: _____

Fluency Score 0 1 2 3

Fluency Scoring Key

0 Reads primarily word-by-word with occasional but infrequent or inappropriate phrasing; no smooth or expressive interpretation, irregular pausing, and no attention to author's meaning or punctuation; no stress or inappropriate stress, and slow rate.

1 Reads primarily in two-word phrases with some three- and four-word groups and some word-by-word reading; almost no smooth, expressive interpretation or pausing guided by author's meaning and punctuation; almost no stress or inappropriate stress, with slow rate most of the time.

2 Reads primarily in three- or four-word phrase groups; some smooth, expressive interpretation and pausing guided by author's meaning and punctuation; mostly appropriate stress and rate with some slowdowns.

3 Reads primarily in larger, meaningful phrases or word groups; mostly smooth, expressive interpretation and pausing guided by author's meaning and punctuation; appropriate stress and rate with only a few slowdowns.

Part Two: Comprehension Conversation

Have a conversation with the student, noting the key understandings the student expresses. Use prompts as needed to stimulate discussion of understandings the student does not express. It is not necessary to use every prompt for each book. Score for evidence of all understandings expressed—with or without a prompt. Circle the number in the score column that reflects the level of understanding demonstrated.

Teacher: Talk about what you learned in this book.

<table>
<tr><td colspan="2">

Comprehension Scoring Key

0   Reflects **unsatisfactory** understanding of the text. Either does not respond or talks off the topic.

1   Reflects **limited** understanding of the text. Mentions a few facts or ideas but does not express the important information or ideas.

2   Reflects **satisfactory** understanding of the text. Includes important information and ideas but neglects other key understandings.

3   Reflects **excellent** understanding of the text. Includes almost all important information and main ideas.

</td></tr>
</table>

Key Understandings	Prompts	Score
Within the Text There are different kinds of trucks and they do different things. (Names 2–3 trucks such as fire truck, trash truck, mail truck, snowplow, food truck, ice cream truck.) Trucks do many different jobs. (Gives 1–3 examples such as: a fire truck has a long hose and puts out fires; a trash truck crushes trash; a mail truck picks up and carries mail; a snowplow carries snow away; some trucks carry food; an ice cream truck sells ice cream and plays a song; a toy truck is for play.) *Note any additional understandings:*	Tell what you learned about trucks from reading this book. Tell me more about different kinds of trucks and the jobs they do.	0 1 2 3
Beyond and About the Text People need trucks because (gives a plausible reason). The toy truck is different from all the other trucks because (gives 2–3 reasons such as it is little; it is used for play; it doesn't do jobs for people). In this book, the author shows trucks that do work and trucks you play with. *Note any additional understandings:*	Why are trucks important to us? How is the truck on the last page different from all the other trucks? Look at the truck on page 16. How is it different from the other trucks in the book?	0 1 2 3

Guide to Total Score

6–7 Excellent Comprehension

5   **Satisfactory** Comprehension

4   **Limited** Comprehension

0–3 Unsatisfactory Comprehension

Subtotal Score: _____ /6

Add 1 for any additional understandings: _____ /1

Total Score: _____ /7

Part Three: Writing About Reading *(optional)*

Read the writing/drawing prompt below to the student. You can also cut the prompt on the dotted line and give it to the child. Specify the amount of time for the student to complete the task on a separate sheet of paper. (See *Assessment Guide* for more information.)

Writing About Reading Scoring Key

0 Reflects **no** understanding of the text.

1 Reflects **very limited** understanding of the text.

2 Reflects **partial** understanding of the text.

3 Reflects **excellent** understanding of the text.

- -

Write about three things you learned about trucks and the important jobs they do. You can draw a picture to go with your writing.

Recording Forms

Student _____   Grade _____   Date _____

Teacher _____   School _____

Recording Form
Part One: Oral Reading

Place the book in front of the student. Read the title and introduction.

Introduction: A boy named Spencer went to a farm to pick out a cat, but he had trouble finding the best cat. Read to find out if Spencer found the best cat for him.

Summary of Scores:	
Accuracy	_____
Self-correction	_____
Fluency	_____
Comprehension	_____
Writing	_____

Sources of Information Used

Page	Text *The Best Cat* Level I, RW: 263, E: 28	E	SC	E			SC		
				M	S	V	M	S	V
2	Spencer wanted a cat more than anything in the world. He wanted a cat that would sleep on his bed and purr in his ear and be his best furry friend.								
3	"Please, can I get a cat?" Spencer asked. "I **really** want one." "Are you sure?" his mother answered. "It is hard work to take care of a cat."								
	Subtotal								

Part One: Oral Reading *continued*

					Sources of Information Used						
					E			SC			
Page	**Text**	E	SC	M	S	V	M	S	V		
4	"I'll take good care of him," said Spencer. "I promise. I'll brush him and feed him and give him water every day." "All right," said his mother. "Let's go to Apple Tree Farm. Maybe we can get a cat there."										
6	Spencer and his mother went to Apple Tree Farm. Many animals lived on the farm. There were cows and horses in the fields. There was a friendly farmer. And there were cats everywhere!										
8	Spencer had never seen so many cats and kittens!										
	Subtotal										

Part One: Oral Reading *continued*

Sources of Information Used

Page	Text	E	SC	E			SC		
				M	S	V	M	S	V
9	"How will you choose just one?" asked Spencer's mother. Spencer thought about it. Then he said, "I'll choose the best cat for me."								
10	Spencer saw a black cat playing on the straw in the barn. "I like your shiny fur," said Spencer. "Will you be my cat?"								
11	The cat ducked under the straw. "I guess you're not the best cat for me," said Spencer. "I'll look for another cat."								
	Subtotal								

Part One: Oral Reading *continued*

Sources of Information Used

Page	Text	E	SC	E			SC		
				M	S	V	M	S	V
12	Spencer watched another cat licking her paw down by the pond. "I like your fluffy tail and your pink tongue," said Spencer. "Will you be my cat?"								
13	The cat didn't even look at Spencer. "I can tell that you are not the best cat for me," Spencer said. "I'll look for another cat."								
	Subtotal								
	Total								

Have the student finish reading the book silently.

Recording Forms

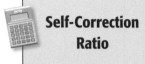

	Errors	**28 or more**	**25–27**	**23–24**	**20–22**	**18–19**	**15–17**	**12–14**	**10–11**	**7–9**	**4–6**	**1–3**	**0**
Accuracy Rate	**%**	Below 90%	90%	91%	92%	93%	94%	95%	96%	97%	98%	99%	100%

Self-Correction Ratio	(E + SC) ÷ SC = 1: _____

Fluency Score	0 1 2 3	**Fluency Scoring Key** **0** Reads primarily word-by-word with occasional but infrequent or inappropriate phrasing; no smooth or expressive interpretation, irregular pausing, and no attention to author's meaning or punctuation; no stress or inappropriate stress, and slow rate. **1** Reads primarily in two-word phrases with some three- and four-word groups and some word-by-word reading; almost no smooth, expressive interpretation or pausing guided by author's meaning and punctuation; almost no stress or inappropriate stress, with slow rate most of the time. **2** Reads primarily in three- or four-word phrase groups; some smooth, expressive interpretation and pausing guided by author's meaning and punctuation; mostly appropriate stress and rate with some slowdowns. **3** Reads primarily in larger, meaningful phrases or word groups; mostly smooth, expressive interpretation and pausing guided by author's meaning and punctuation; appropriate stress and rate with only a few slowdowns.

Part Two: Comprehension Conversation

Have a conversation with the student, noting the key understandings the student expresses. Use prompts as needed to stimulate discussion of understandings the student does not express. It is not necessary to use every prompt for each book. Score for evidence of all understandings expressed—with or without a prompt. Circle the number in the score column that reflects the level of understanding demonstrated.

Teacher: Talk about what happened in this story.

Comprehension Scoring Key
0 Reflects **unsatisfactory** understanding of the text. Either does not respond or talks off the topic.
1 Reflects **limited** understanding of the text. Mentions a few facts or ideas but does not express the important information or ideas.
2 Reflects **satisfactory** understanding of the text. Includes important information and ideas but neglects other key understandings.
3 Reflects **excellent** understanding of the text. Includes almost all important information and main ideas.

Key Understandings	Prompts	Score
Within the Text Spencer went to a farm to get a cat but he could not find one. Finally, he did find a cat. Recounts some essential information from the text, such as: the boy went to the farm to choose a cat; something was wrong with all the cats he saw; finally, a little cat chose him. *Note any additional understandings:*	What was the problem in the story? How was Spencer's problem solved? Tell what the boy did to find the best cat for him.	0 1 2 3
Beyond and About the Text Spencer really wanted a cat because (gives a plausible reason). Spencer was disappointed (or sad) when none of the cats at the farm were the right cat. The little cat wanted a home and the cat really chose the boy. Spencer was glad the cat chose him. You can tell Spencer really wanted a cat because it showed *really* in dark letters and he was thinking about a cat (or other feature of the text that the child has noticed). *Note any additional understandings:*	Tell why you think Spencer wanted a cat (or what kind of cat the boy really wanted). Tell how Spencer felt when he couldn't find a cat (or how he felt at the end). Why do you think the little cat was the best cat for Spencer? How did Spencer feel at the end? Look at page 3. How did the author and illustrator show you how much Spencer wanted a cat?	0 1 2 3

Guide to Total Score
6–7 Excellent Comprehension
5   **Satisfactory** Comprehension
4   **Limited** Comprehension
0–3 Unsatisfactory Comprehension

Subtotal Score: ____ /6

Add 1 for any additional understandings: _____ /1

Total Score: _____ /7

Part Three: Writing About Reading (optional)

Read the writing/drawing prompt below to the student. You can also cut the prompt on the dotted line and give it to the child. Specify the amount of time for the student to complete the task on a separate sheet of paper. (See *Assessment Guide* for more information.)

Writing About Reading Scoring Key
0 Reflects **no** understanding of the text.
1 Reflects **very limited** understanding of the text.
2 Reflects **partial** understanding of the text.
3 Reflects **excellent** understanding of the text.

— —

Write about Spencer and how he found the best cat. You can draw a picture to go with your writing.

Student _____ Grade _____ Date _____

Teacher _____ School _____

Recording Form
Part One: Oral Reading

Place the book in front of the student. Read the title and introduction.

Introduction: Koalas are animals that live in a country called Australia. Read this book to learn all about how koalas live, what they eat, and about their babies.

Sources of Information Used

Page	Text *All About Koalas* Level I, RW: 217, E: 23	E	SC	E			SC		
				M	S	V	M	S	V
2	This is a koala. It comes from Australia.								
3	Koalas live in tall trees called gum trees. Koalas have sharp claws. The claws help them climb the trees.								
4	Koalas have thick fur and white chests.								
5	They have fluffy ears and big noses!								
	Subtotal								

Part One: Oral Reading *continued*

Sources of Information Used

Page	Text	E	SC	E			SC		
				M	S	V	M	S	V
6	The koala's nose helps it find food. Koalas eat gum leaves.								
7	Koalas sleep in the day. At night, they wake up to eat.								
8	Koalas do not drink water. There is water in the leaves koalas eat. They get food and water at the same time.								
9	This is a baby koala. A young koala is called a joey, just like a baby kangaroo. When a joey is born, it has no hair.								
	Subtotal								

Part One: Oral Reading *continued*

Sources of Information Used

Page	Text	E	SC	E			SC		
				M	S	V	M	S	V
10	A koala joey is very small. The little koala stays in its mother's special pouch.								
11	In the pouch, the baby koala drinks its mother's milk.								
12	This joey is seven months old. It is as long as a loaf of bread.								
13	The joey travels on its mother's back. It uses its thumbs to hold on.								
	Subtotal								

Part One: Oral Reading *continued*

Sources of Information Used

Page	Text	E	SC	E			SC		
				M	S	V	M	S	V
14	Koalas "talk" to each other. Mothers and babies make soft sounds. Koalas make deep sounds when they are far away.								
15	Koalas have a problem today. Some people are cutting down trees to make room for houses.								
16	Many people want to save these trees. Koalas need a safe place to call home.								
	Subtotal								
	Total								

Accuracy Rate	**Errors**	**23 or more**	**21–22**	**19–20**	**17–18**	**15–16**	**12–14**	**10–11**	**8–9**	**6–7**	**4–5**	**1–3**	**0**
	%	Below 90%	90%	91%	92%	93%	94%	95%	96%	97%	98%	99%	100%

Self-Correction Ratio	$(E + SC) \div SC = 1:$ ____

Fluency Score	0 1 2 3	**Fluency Scoring Key**

Fluency Scoring Key

0 Reads primarily word-by-word with occasional but infrequent or inappropriate phrasing; no smooth or expressive interpretation, irregular pausing, and no attention to author's meaning or punctuation; no stress or inappropriate stress, and slow rate.

1 Reads primarily in two-word phrases with some three- and four-word groups and some word-by-word reading; almost no smooth, expressive interpretation or pausing guided by author's meaning and punctuation; almost no stress or inappropriate stress, with slow rate most of the time.

2 Reads primarily in three- or four-word phrase groups; some smooth, expressive interpretation and pausing guided by author's meaning and punctuation; mostly appropriate stress and rate with some slowdowns.

3 Reads primarily in larger, meaningful phrases or word groups; mostly smooth, expressive interpretation and pausing guided by author's meaning and punctuation; appropriate stress and rate with only a few slowdowns.

Recording Forms

Part Two: Comprehension Conversation

Have a conversation with the student, noting the key understandings the student expresses. Use prompts as needed to stimulate discussion of understandings the student does not express. It is not necessary to use every prompt for each book. Score for evidence of all understandings expressed—with or without a prompt. Circle the number in the score column that reflects the level of understanding demonstrated.

Teacher: Talk about what you learned in this book.

Comprehension Scoring Key
0 Reflects **unsatisfactory** understanding of the text. Either does not respond or talks off the topic.
1 Reflects **limited** understanding of the text. Mentions a few facts or ideas but does not express the important information or ideas.
2 Reflects **satisfactory** understanding of the text. Includes important information and ideas but neglects other key understandings.
3 Reflects **excellent** understanding of the text. Includes almost all important information and main ideas.

Key Understandings	Prompts	Score
Within the Text Names several facts about koalas such as: live in tall gum trees; have sharp claws; have thick fur and white chests; have fluffy ears; eat leaves; sleep in the day; don't drink water; have babies called joeys that don't have any hair. *Note any additional understandings:*	Talk about what you learned about koalas. What else did you learn?	0 1 2 3
Beyond and About the Text Koalas are like kangaroos (or any plausible comparison). Koalas' bodies help them climb tall trees. A baby koala could not live by itself; it has to be in the mother's pouch because it is so young (or little). Trees are important to koalas because they are safe there and they eat the leaves. The author doesn't want people to cut down the trees because it would be bad for koalas. *Note any additional understandings:*	Do koalas remind you of any other animals? What helps the koalas climb tall trees? Why does the joey stay in the mother's pouch? Why are trees important to koalas? Look at page 15. Why do you think the author is telling us about cutting down the trees?	0 1 2 3

Guide to Total Score
6–7 Excellent Comprehension
5   **Satisfactory** Comprehension
4   **Limited** Comprehension
0–3 Unsatisfactory Comprehension

Subtotal Score: _____ /6

Add 1 for any additional understandings: _____ /1

Total Score: _____ /7

Part Three: Writing About Reading *(optional)*

Read the writing/drawing prompt below to the student. You can also cut the prompt on the dotted line and give it to the child. Specify the amount of time for the student to complete the task on a separate sheet of paper. (See *Assessment Guide* for more information.)

Writing About Reading Scoring Key
0 Reflects **no** understanding of the text.
1 Reflects **very limited** understanding of the text.
2 Reflects **partial** understanding of the text.
3 Reflects **excellent** understanding of the text.

Write about three interesting things you learned about koalas. You can draw a picture to go with your writing.

Student _____   Grade _____   Date _____

Teacher _____   School _____

Recording Form

Part One: Oral Reading

Place the book in front of the student. Read the title and introduction.

Introduction: Ben's family and the other families on the street got a note from their new neighbors. In the note their new neighbors invited them to see their surprise horses. Read to find out what kind of horses they were.

Summary of Scores:	
Accuracy	_____
Self-correction	_____
Fluency	_____
Comprehension	_____
Writing	_____

Sources of Information Used

Page	Start Time _____ min. _____ sec. *Our New Neighbors* Level J, RW: 224, E: 24	E	SC	E			SC		
				M	S	V	M	S	V
2	On Saturday morning, Ben saw an envelope on the front steps. "Mom, Dad, Polly!" he called. "Look what I found!"								
3	Dad read the note that was inside. Hello Neighbors, We just moved into the big house on the corner. Please come to a party next Saturday at 10 o'clock. We want to meet you <u>and</u> we want you to meet our horses. Max and Flo								
	Subtotal								

Part One: Oral Reading *continued*

Sources of Information Used

Page	Text	E	SC	E			SC		
				M	S	V	M	S	V
4	"Horses?" Everyone looked at one another. "Horses on our street?" asked Dad.								
5	"I hope they're ponies," said Ben. "When we have birthday parties, we can have pony rides." "I hope they're big white horses," said Polly. "Maybe they'll give us a ride."								
6	"Well," said Mom, "that house on the corner is just right for horses. It has a big yard. And there's that red barn in back."								
7	"Look," said Ben. "The neighbors are reading a note, too!" Mom and Dad called across the street.								
	Subtotal								

Part One: Oral Reading *continued*

Sources of Information Used

Page	Text	E	SC	E			SC		
				M	S	V	M	S	V
7 *cont.*	Did you get the note about the horses?" Dad asked.								
8	"What do you think it's all about?" Mom asked the neighbor. "I don't know," he said. "I don't think that barn is big enough for horses."								
9	Another neighbor popped her head over the fence. "I can tell you something else," she said. "Every day when I pass that house, I hear loud noises, like someone is hammering." All the neighbors were excited about the mystery.								
	Subtotal								
	End Time ____ min. ____ sec. **Total**								

Have the student finish reading the book silently.

Accuracy Rate	Errors	24 or more	22–23	20–21	17–19	15–16	13–14	11–12	8–10	6–7	4–5	1–3	0
	%	Below 90%	90%	91%	92%	93%	94%	95%	96%	97%	98%	99%	100%

Self-Correction Ratio	(E + SC) ÷ SC = 1: _____

Fluency Score	0 1 2 3

Fluency Scoring Key

0 Reads primarily word-by-word with occasional but infrequent or inappropriate phrasing; no smooth or expressive interpretation, irregular pausing, and no attention to author's meaning or punctuation; no stress or inappropriate stress, and slow rate.

1 Reads primarily in two-word phrases with some three- and four-word groups and some word-by-word reading; almost no smooth, expressive interpretation or pausing guided by author's meaning and punctuation; almost no stress or inappropriate stress, with slow rate most of the time.

2 Reads primarily in three- or four-word phrase groups; some smooth, expressive interpretation and pausing guided by author's meaning and punctuation; mostly appropriate stress and rate with some slowdowns.

3 Reads primarily in larger, meaningful phrases or word groups; mostly smooth, expressive interpretation and pausing guided by author's meaning and punctuation; appropriate stress and rate with only a few slowdowns.

Reading Rate
(Optional)

End Time   _____ min. _____ sec.

Start Time   _____ min. _____ sec.

Total Time   _____ min. _____ sec.

Total Seconds   _____

(RW × 60) ÷ Total Seconds = Words Per Minute (WPM)

13,440 ÷ _____ = _____ WPM

Part Two: Comprehension Conversation

Have a conversation with the student, noting the key understandings the student expresses. Use prompts as needed to stimulate discussion of understandings the student does not express. It is not necessary to use every prompt for each book. Score for evidence of all understandings expressed—with or without a prompt. Circle the number in the score column that reflects the level of understanding demonstrated.

Teacher: Talk about what happened in this story.

<table>
<tr><td>Comprehension Scoring Key</td></tr>
<tr><td>0 Reflects unsatisfactory understanding of the text. Either does not respond or talks off the topic.</td></tr>
<tr><td>1 Reflects limited understanding of the text. Mentions a few facts or ideas but does not express the important information or ideas.</td></tr>
<tr><td>2 Reflects satisfactory understanding of the text. Includes important information and ideas but neglects other key understandings.</td></tr>
<tr><td>3 Reflects excellent understanding of the text. Includes almost all important information and main ideas.</td></tr>
</table>

Key Understandings	Prompts	Score
Within the Text Recounts most of the important events such as: the new neighbors invited everyone to see their horses; everyone was asking what kind of horses the neighbors had; the horses turned out to be a merry-go-round (or carousel). *Note any additional understandings:*	What was the mystery in the story? What did the new neighbors do to get everyone interested in their horses? What happened when people got the note? What happened at the end?	0 1 2 3
Beyond and About the Text The new neighbors wanted to surprise everyone so they kept the horses a secret. Everyone was wondering about the horses and imagining the kinds of horses they were. Clues before the last page are: "loud hammering noises," "music playing," "two horses going up and two going down," "four horses going around and around." All through the book there were clues to help you predict that it was a merry-go-round. (Points out several in the text, i.e., barn not big enough, hammering noise.) *Note any additional understandings:*	Why did the new neighbors keep the horses a secret? What were the people in the neighborhood thinking about the horses? There were a few clues that might have helped you guess what kind of horses were in the barn. Can you think of any? Can you show me some of the pages where the author gave you clues that it might be a merry-go-round in the barn?	0 1 2 3

Guide to Total Score

6–7 **Excellent** Comprehension

5 **Satisfactory** Comprehension

4 **Limited** Comprehension

0–3 **Unsatisfactory** Comprehension

Subtotal Score: _____ /6

Add 1 for any additional understandings: _____ /1

Total Score: _____ /7

Part Three: Writing About Reading *(optional)*

Read the writing/drawing prompt below to the student. You can also cut the prompt on the dotted line and give it to the child. Specify the amount of time for the student to complete the task on a separate sheet of paper. (See *Assessment Guide* for more information.)

<table>
<tr><td>Writing About Reading Scoring Key</td></tr>
<tr><td>0 Reflects no understanding of the text.</td></tr>
<tr><td>1 Reflects very limited understanding of the text.</td></tr>
<tr><td>2 Reflects partial understanding of the text.</td></tr>
<tr><td>3 Reflects excellent understanding of the text.</td></tr>
</table>

- -

Write about the horses and how the new neighbors made them a surprise for everyone. You can draw a picture to go with your writing.

Student _____   Grade _____   Date _____

Teacher _____   School _____

Recording Form
Part One: Oral Reading

Place the book in front of the student. Read the title and introduction.

Summary of Scores:	
Accuracy	_____
Self-correction	_____
Fluency	_____
Comprehension	_____
Writing	_____

Introduction: Dogs can be more than pets. They can help people. Therapy dogs help people feel better, and service dogs help people do things. Read to find out about these two kinds of dogs and what they do.

Sources of Information Used

Page	Start Time ____ min. ____ sec. *More Than a Pet* Level J, RW: 267, E: 28	E	SC	E M	E S	E V	SC M	SC S	SC V
2	Do you know anyone who has a pet dog? Maybe you have a dog in your family. Dogs are good pets.								
3	Some dogs are more than pets. Two kinds of dogs do special jobs. Dogs that make people feel better are called **therapy dogs**. Dogs that work are called **service dogs**.								
4	Therapy Dogs Sometimes people can not stay at home because they								
	Subtotal								

Part One: Oral Reading *continued*

Sources of Information Used

Page	Text	E	SC	E			SC		
				M	S	V	M	S	V
4 *cont.*	are not well. They must stay in a hospital or in a nursing home. They miss their homes and families. People feel better when they pet a dog.								
7	People like to pet dogs and feel their soft fur. Therapy dogs cheer people up when they are sad because they are not feeling well.								
8	May is a friendly and snuggly dog. She visits Sam in the hospital. She curls right up in bed, and Sam smiles.								
	Subtotal								

Recording Forms

Part One: Oral Reading *continued*

Sources of Information Used

Page	Text	E	SC	E			SC		
				M	S	V	M	S	V
9	Addie is a gentle pup. Her owner takes her to visit people in a nursing home. She stays very still when they pet her.								
10	Service Dogs Service dogs are more than pets. Service dogs live with the people they help. They work, play, and go everywhere with their owners.								
11	Service dogs go to a special school where they are trained to help their owners.								
	Subtotal								

Part One: Oral Reading *continued*

Sources of Information Used

Page	Text	E	SC	E			SC		
				M	S	V	M	S	V
12	Royal is a service dog who helps Lily, his owner. Lily needs help because she can't see well. Royal came to live with Lily when he was a puppy. He and Lily were trained together. Now, Royal and Lily are together all the time. Lily holds on to Royal's harness at the mall or on the train. Royal makes sure it's safe for Lily to walk.								
	Subtotal								
	End Time ____ min. ____ sec. **Total**								

Have the student finish reading the book silently.

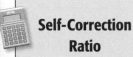

Accuracy Rate	Errors	28 or more	25–27	23–24	20–22	18–19	15–17	12–14	10–11	8–9	5–7	1–4	0
	%	Below 90%	90%	91%	92%	93%	94%	95%	96%	97%	98%	99%	100%

Self-Correction Ratio

$$(E + SC) \div SC = 1: \underline{\quad}$$

Fluency Score   0   1   2   3

Fluency Scoring Key

0 Reads primarily word-by-word with occasional but infrequent or inappropriate phrasing; no smooth or expressive interpretation, irregular pausing, and no attention to author's meaning or punctuation; no stress or inappropriate stress, and slow rate.

1 Reads primarily in two-word phrases with some three- and four-word groups and some word-by-word reading; almost no smooth, expressive interpretation or pausing guided by author's meaning and punctuation; almost no stress or inappropriate stress, with slow rate most of the time.

2 Reads primarily in three- or four-word phrase groups; some smooth, expressive interpretation and pausing guided by author's meaning and punctuation; mostly appropriate stress and rate with some slowdowns.

3 Reads primarily in larger, meaningful phrases or word groups; mostly smooth, expressive interpretation and pausing guided by author's meaning and punctuation; appropriate stress and rate with only a few slowdowns.

Reading Rate *(Optional)*

End Time   _____ min. _____ sec.

Start Time   _____ min. _____ sec.

Total Time   _____ min. _____ sec.

Total Seconds   _____

(RW × 60) ÷ Total Seconds = Words Per Minute (WPM)

16,020 ÷ _____ = _____ WPM

Part Two: Comprehension Conversation

Have a conversation with the student, noting the key understandings the student expresses. Use prompts as needed to stimulate discussion of understandings the student does not express. It is not necessary to use every prompt for each book. Score for evidence of all understandings expressed—with or without a prompt. Circle the number in the score column that reflects the level of understanding demonstrated.

Teacher: Talk about what you learned in this book.

Comprehension Scoring Key	
0	Reflects **unsatisfactory** understanding of the text. Either does not respond or talks off the topic.
1	Reflects **limited** understanding of the text. Mentions a few facts or ideas but does not express the important information or ideas.
2	Reflects **satisfactory** understanding of the text. Includes important information and ideas but neglects other key understandings.
3	Reflects **excellent** understanding of the text. Includes almost all important information and main ideas.

Key Understandings	Prompts	Score
Within the Text There are two kinds of dogs that help people. Some dogs help people feel better and some dogs work. (May or may not use the terms *therapy* and *service*.) Dogs help people in many different ways. (Gives 2–3 examples such as: dogs cheer people up; they help their owners; they make sure the owner is safe; they get things for their owners.) *Note any additional understandings:*	What were the two kinds of dogs that you read about? What did you learn about therapy dogs? What did you learn about service dogs? What else did you learn about the two kinds of dogs?	0 1 2 3
Beyond and About the Text Dogs must be smart because they can learn to help people in different ways (or people train them). Dogs are good pets and they can also do a lot more things to help people. In this picture, the woman is blind and the dog is helping her get on a train. The heading helped me know what kind of dog I would be reading about. *Note any additional understandings:*	Why do you think dogs can be so helpful? Why do you think dogs are so important to people? Look at the photograph on page 13. What information does it give you? Look at page 4. How does the heading "Therapy Dogs" (point to it) help you?	0 1 2 3

Guide to Total Score	
6–7	**Excellent** Comprehension
5	**Satisfactory** Comprehension
4	**Limited** Comprehension
0–3	**Unsatisfactory** Comprehension

Subtotal Score: _____ /6

Add 1 for any additional understandings: _____ /1

Total Score: _____ /7

Part Three: Writing About Reading *(optional)*

Read the writing/drawing prompt below to the student. You can also cut the prompt on the dotted line and give it to the child. Specify the amount of time for the student to complete the task on a separate sheet of paper. (See *Assessment Guide* for more information.)

Writing About Reading Scoring Key	
0	Reflects **no** understanding of the text.
1	Reflects **very limited** understanding of the text.
2	Reflects **partial** understanding of the text.
3	Reflects **excellent** understanding of the text.

- -

Write about three ways dogs help people. You can draw a picture to go with your writing.

Student _____ Grade _____ Date _____

Teacher _____ School _____

Recording Form
Part One: Oral Reading

Place the book in front of the student. Read the title and introduction.

Introduction: Edwin's hair was so long that he looked like his dog Ruff. His mom and dad gave him a haircut, and it was so bad he had to wear a wig hat. Read to find out what happened.

Summary of Scores:	
Accuracy	_____
Self-correction	_____
Fluency	_____
Comprehension	_____
Writing	_____

Sources of Information Used

Page	Start Time ____ min. ____ sec. *Edwin's Haircut* Level K, RW: 234, E: 25	E	SC	E			SC		
				M	S	V	M	S	V
2	"Good morning, Edwin," Dad said. He was talking to Edwin's dog, Ruff. Then he turned to Edwin. "Good morning, Ruff," he said to his shaggy son.								
3	He could tell that his dad was only joking, but Edwin did not laugh or smile. Instead, he pushed his hair off his face and said, "I'm not Ruff. I'm EDWIN! See? Ruff is the one with the tail." "Why, I think you are right," answered Dad. "I don't know how I could have mixed you up with Ruff." "I know how," said Mom. "It's time for a haircut!"								
4	Mom put some newspapers on the floor and sat Edwin in a chair. Then she was ready to cut Edwin's hair.								
	Subtotal								

Part One: Oral Reading *continued*

Sources of Information Used

Page	Text	E	SC	E			SC		
				M	S	V	M	S	V
5	Snip! Mom took a little off the top. Snip! She took some off the back. Then she cut a lot off the sides. "It doesn't look right," said Dad. "One side is too long. Let me try." Snip! went Dad.								
6	"Now the other side is too long," Mom complained. "Let's see if I can fix it." Snip! Snip! "It's still not right," said Dad. "Let me take a bit more off this side."								
7	Edwin's mom and dad took turns snipping and trimming, but the more they snipped, the worse things got. Edwin's hair got more and more crooked. "We'd better quit," said Mom. Dad agreed. "If we don't, he's not going to have any hair left!" he said.								
	Subtotal								
	End Time ____ min. ____ sec. **Total**								

Have the student finish reading the book silently.

Accuracy Rate	Errors	25 or more	23–24	20–22	18–19	16–17	13–15	11–12	9–10	6–8	4–5	1–3	0
	%	Below 90%	90%	91%	92%	93%	94%	95%	96%	97%	98%	99%	100%

Self-Correction Ratio

(E + SC) ÷ SC = 1: _____

Fluency Score

0   1   2   3

Fluency Scoring Key

0   Reads primarily word-by-word with occasional but infrequent or inappropriate phrasing; no smooth or expressive interpretation, irregular pausing, and no attention to author's meaning or punctuation; no stress or inappropriate stress, and slow rate.

1   Reads primarily in two-word phrases with some three- and four-word groups and some word-by-word reading; almost no smooth, expressive interpretation or pausing guided by author's meaning and punctuation; almost no stress or inappropriate stress, with slow rate most of the time.

2   Reads primarily in three- or four-word phrase groups; some smooth, expressive interpretation and pausing guided by author's meaning and punctuation; mostly appropriate stress and rate with some slowdowns.

3   Reads primarily in larger, meaningful phrases or word groups; mostly smooth, expressive interpretation and pausing guided by author's meaning and punctuation; appropriate stress and rate with only a few slowdowns.

Reading Rate *(Optional)*

End Time   _____ min. _____ sec.

Start Time   _____ min. _____ sec.

Total Time   _____ min. _____ sec.

Total Seconds   _____

(RW × 60) ÷ Total Seconds = Words Per Minute (WPM)

14,040 ÷ _____ = _____ WPM

Part Two: Comprehension Conversation

Have a conversation with the student, noting the key understandings the student expresses. Use prompts as needed to stimulate discussion of understandings the student does not express. It is not necessary to use every prompt for each book. Score for evidence of all understandings expressed—with or without a prompt. Circle the number in the score column that reflects the level of understanding demonstrated.

Teacher: Talk about what happened in this story.

Key Understandings	Prompts	Score
Within the Text Edwin got a terrible haircut and had to wear a wig hat (or wig) all of the time. Recounts most of the important events such as: Edwin needed a haircut so his mom and dad gave him one; his hair looked awful; he had to wear a wig hat everywhere; his hair grew out again but he wouldn't let his mom cut it; he said that next time he would pick the barber to give him his haircut. *Note any additional understandings:*	What was the problem in this story? How did Edwin and his parents solve the problem? What happened at the end?	0 1 2 3
Beyond and About the Text Edwin hated his haircut. It was so bad that he was embarrassed to go to school. Edwin didn't care if other kids teased him about his wig hat. He just went on and did everything he always did. Edwin stuck up for himself in the end when he said he would pick the barber next time. The beginning and ending of the story were alike because he needed a haircut, but in the end Edwin changed his mind about who should cut his hair. Some ways the author made this story funny were (any specific pages where the words or illustrations show humor). *Note any additional understandings:*	How do you think Edwin felt when he first looked at himself with his new haircut? What kind of kid was Edwin? What was he like? What makes you think that? Edwin acted differently at the end of the story than he did at the beginning. What did he do that was different? How were the beginning and ending parts of this story alike? How were they different? This author and illustrator wanted to make *Edwin's Haircut* a very funny book. Can you show me some parts that are funny?	0 1 2 3

Guide to Total Score

6–7   **Excellent** Comprehension

5   **Satisfactory** Comprehension

4   **Limited** Comprehension

0–3   **Unsatisfactory** Comprehension

Subtotal Score: _____ /6

Add 1 for any additional understandings: _____ /1

Total Score: _____ /7

Part Three: Writing About Reading *(optional)*

Read the writing/drawing prompt below to the student. You can also cut the prompt on the dotted line and give it to the child. Specify the amount of time for the student to complete the task on a separate sheet of paper. (See *Assessment Guide* for more information.)

Writing About Reading Scoring Key
0 Reflects **no** understanding of the text.
1 Reflects **very limited** understanding of the text.
2 Reflects **partial** understanding of the text.
3 Reflects **excellent** understanding of the text.

— —

At the end of the story, Edwin decided to have his hair cut by a barber. Do you think this was a good idea? Write about why or why not. You can draw a picture to go with your writing.

Student _____   Grade _____   Date _____

Teacher _____   School _____

Recording Form
Part One: Oral Reading

Place the book in front of the student. Read the title and introduction.

Introduction: Animals and people have five senses. But animal senses do not always work like people's senses work. Read to find out how some animals see, touch, taste, smell, and hear.

Summary of Scores:	
Accuracy	_____
Self-correction	_____
Fluency	_____
Comprehension	_____
Writing	_____

Sources of Information Used

Page	Start Time ____ min. ____ sec. *Surprising Animal Senses* Level K, RW: 271, E: 29	E	SC	E			SC		
				M	S	V	M	S	V
2	Introduction								
	You may already know about your five senses. People can see, touch, taste, smell, and hear.								
	Animals also use their senses to learn about the world. But animal senses do not always work the way people's senses work.								
	In this book you will read about how animal senses work—how many animals see, touch, taste, smell, and hear in ways that are different from people.								
	Subtotal								

Part One: Oral Reading *continued*

Sources of Information Used

Page	Text	E	SC	E			SC		
				M	S	V	M	S	V
4	Sight Who is the mother and who is the child in this picture? How can you tell? You use your sense of sight.								
5	You use your eyes to see. A starfish uses its arms! Starfish do not have eyes. Instead, they have small spots at the ends of their arms to help them see light and dark.								
6	Touch If your eyes are closed, how can you tell the difference between a soft chick and rough sandpaper? You use your sense of touch.								
7	You use your skin to touch. Cats do, too. But cats also use their whiskers! The touch of the whiskers helps cats know whether they can fit through small openings.								
	Subtotal								

Part One: Oral Reading *continued*

Sources of Information Used

Page	Text	E	SC	E M	E S	E V	SC M	SC S	SC V
8	Taste How can you tell if you like salad? You use your sense of taste.								
9	You use your tongue to taste. A butterfly tastes with its feet! When butterflies land on flowers, they use taste buds on their feet to know if the flowers are good to eat.								
10	Smell Do you like the smell of fresh flowers? Most people do. Your sense of smell tells you that flowers smell good.								
11	You use your nose to smell. Snakes use their mouths! Instead of sniffing, they flick their tongues to bring smells into their mouths.								
	Subtotal								
	End Time _____ min. _____ sec. Total								

Have the student finish reading the book silently.

Accuracy Rate	Errors	29 or more	27–28	24–26	21–23	19–20	16–18	13–15	10–12	8–9	5–7	1–4	0
	%	Below 90%	90%	91%	92%	93%	94%	95%	96%	97%	98%	99%	100%

Self-Correction Ratio

(E + SC) ÷ SC = 1: _____

Fluency Score

0 1 2 3

Fluency Scoring Key

0 Reads primarily word-by-word with occasional but infrequent or inappropriate phrasing; no smooth or expressive interpretation, irregular pausing, and no attention to author's meaning or punctuation; no stress or inappropriate stress, and slow rate.

1 Reads primarily in two-word phrases with some three- and four-word groups and some word-by-word reading; almost no smooth, expressive interpretation or pausing guided by author's meaning and punctuation; almost no stress or inappropriate stress, with slow rate most of the time.

2 Reads primarily in three- or four-word phrase groups; some smooth, expressive interpretation and pausing guided by author's meaning and punctuation; mostly appropriate stress and rate with some slowdowns.

3 Reads primarily in larger, meaningful phrases or word groups; mostly smooth, expressive interpretation and pausing guided by author's meaning and punctuation; appropriate stress and rate with only a few slowdowns.

Reading Rate *(Optional)*

End Time   _____ min. _____ sec.

Start Time   _____ min. _____ sec.

Total Time   _____ min. _____ sec.

Total Seconds   _____

(RW × 60) ÷ Total Seconds = Words Per Minute (WPM)

16,260 ÷ _____ = _____ WPM

Part Two: Comprehension Conversation

Have a conversation with the student, noting the key understandings the student expresses. Use prompts as needed to stimulate discussion of understandings the student does not express. It is not necessary to use every prompt for each book. Score for evidence of all understandings expressed—with or without a prompt. Circle the number in the score column that reflects the level of understanding demonstrated.

Teacher: Talk about what you learned in this book.

Comprehension Scoring Key
0 Reflects **unsatisfactory** understanding of the text. Either does not respond or talks off the topic.
1 Reflects **limited** understanding of the text. Mentions a few facts or ideas but does not express the important information or ideas.
2 Reflects **satisfactory** understanding of the text. Includes important information and ideas but neglects other key understandings.
3 Reflects **excellent** understanding of the text. Includes almost all important information and main ideas.

Key Understandings	Prompts	Score
Within the Text People and animals have senses. Some animals use their senses in different ways than people. Reports 2–3 details about how animals use their senses such as: a starfish uses its arms to see; a cat uses its whiskers to feel; a butterfly uses its feet to taste; a snake uses its tongue to smell; a cricket uses its front legs to hear; some animals have super senses that are stronger than people's. *Note any additional understandings:*	What did you learn about animals and their senses? How are animals' senses the same as people's senses? How do some animals use their senses? How else? Tell about some examples from this book.	0 1 2 3
Beyond and About the Text Reports one cause/effect relationship such as, dogs are good at tracking people because they can smell a million times better than people. Animals can do things people cannot do because of their senses. (Gives an example such as: birds can see from high in the sky; bloodhounds can track a person's smell; bats can listen to know where they are in the dark.) The heading "Super Senses" means that all these animals have a super sense of some kind that is stronger than ours. The child shows pages in the book (i.e., people use skin to touch and cats use whiskers, people use tongues to taste and butterflies use their feet). *Note any additional understandings:*	Why do animals need these special senses? Can animals' senses help them do things people cannot do? How? What is an example? Look at the heading "Super Senses" on page 14 (point to it). What does this heading tell you about the information in this section? This author compares people's senses and animals' senses. Can you show me a page where the author tells about people senses and animal senses?	0 1 2 3

Guide to Total Score	
6–7	**Excellent** Comprehension
5	**Satisfactory** Comprehension
4	**Limited** Comprehension
0–3	**Unsatisfactory** Comprehension

Subtotal Score: _____ /6

Add 1 for any additional understandings: _____ /1

Total Score: _____ /7

Part Three: Writing About Reading *(optional)*

Read the writing/drawing prompt below to the student. You can also cut the prompt on the dotted line and give it to the child. Specify the amount of time for the student to complete the task on a separate sheet of paper. (See *Assessment Guide* for more information.)

Writing About Reading Scoring Key
0 Reflects **no** understanding of the text.
1 Reflects **very limited** understanding of the text.
2 Reflects **partial** understanding of the text.
3 Reflects **excellent** understanding of the text.

Write about three animals and how they use their senses. You can draw a picture to go with your writing.

Student _____ Grade _____ Date _____

Teacher _____ School _____

Recording Form
Part One: Oral Reading

Summary of Scores:

Accuracy _____

Self-correction _____

Fluency _____

Comprehension _____

Writing _____

Place the book in front of the student. Read the title and introduction.

Introduction: April was reading a book about a dog who rescued a man. She decided to write a letter to her favorite author, Julia Reed. She wanted the author to write a book about her dog, Golden Boy. Read to find out what happened.

Sources of Information Used

Page	Start Time _____ min. _____ sec. *Dog Stories* Level L, RW: 267, E: 15	E	SC	E			SC		
				M	S	V	M	S	V
2	April Bailey was reading to her dog, Golden Boy. Her voice got more excited as she read the last few lines.								
3	"*Roxy to the Rescue* is the best book ever!" April told Golden Boy. April was always having Big Ideas, and she had one right then and there.								
4	"I'm going to write a letter to Julia Reed to tell her how much I love this book," April said. "Who's Julia Reed?" her brother Scott asked.								
	Subtotal								

Part One: Oral Reading *continued*

Sources of Information Used

Page	Text	E	SC	E			SC		
				M	S	V	M	S	V
5	"She's my favorite author," April said. "All of her books are about dogs, right, Golden Boy?"								
6	April finished her letter and read it out loud. Golden Boy turned his head. He seemed to be listening.								
7	November 8 Dear Ms. Reed, *Roxy to the Rescue* is your best book yet! I have a Lab named Golden Boy. He's super smart, and he is a super-sniffer! Please would you write about Golden Boy next? He would be a wonderful dog hero. Your biggest fan, April Bailey								
	Subtotal								

Recording Forms

Part One: Oral Reading *continued*

Sources of Information Used

Page	Text	E	SC	E			SC		
				M	S	V	M	S	V
8	April put a photograph of Golden Boy in the envelope, along with her letter. "Hey, don't get your hopes up," warned Scott. "She may get a zillion letters a day."								
9	"I just know Julia Reed will answer me," April said. "She's a dog lover, just like me." She stuck a stamp on the envelope. It was a dog stamp, of course!								
10	"Find your leash, Boy," April told her dog. "Let's go mail this letter." Golden Boy put his nose to the floor, sniffing. Then he dove behind a chair. When he came back out, the missing leash was dangling from his mouth. "That's my super-sniffer!" April said.								
	Subtotal								
End Time ____ min. ____ sec.	**Total**								

Have the student finish reading the book silently.

Accuracy Rate	Errors	15 or more	13–14	10–12	7–9	5–6	1–4	0
	%	Below 95%	95%	96%	97%	98%	99%	100%

Self-Corrections

_____

Fluency Score   0   1   2   3

Fluency Scoring Key

0   Reads primarily word-by-word with occasional but infrequent or inappropriate phrasing; no smooth or expressive interpretation, irregular pausing, and no attention to author's meaning or punctuation; no stress or inappropriate stress, and slow rate.

1   Reads primarily in two-word phrases with some three- and four-word groups and some word-by-word reading; almost no smooth, expressive interpretation or pausing guided by author's meaning and punctuation; almost no stress or inappropriate stress, with slow rate most of the time.

2   Reads primarily in three- or four-word phrase groups; some smooth, expressive interpretation and pausing guided by author's meaning and punctuation; mostly appropriate stress and rate with some slowdowns.

3   Reads primarily in larger, meaningful phrases or word groups; mostly smooth, expressive interpretation and pausing guided by author's meaning and punctuation; appropriate stress and rate with only a few slowdowns.

Reading Rate
(Optional)

End Time   _____ min. _____ sec.

Start Time   _____ min. _____ sec.

Total Time   _____ min. _____ sec.

Total Seconds   _____

(RW × 60) ÷ Total Seconds = Words Per Minute (WPM)

16,020 ÷ _____ = _____ WPM

Part Two: Comprehension Conversation

Have a conversation with the student, noting the key understandings the student expresses. Use prompts as needed to stimulate discussion of understandings the student does not express. It is not necessary to use every prompt for each book. Score for evidence of all understandings expressed–with or without a prompt. Circle the number in the score column that reflects the level of understanding demonstrated.

Teacher: Talk about what happened in this story.

Comprehension Scoring Key
0 Reflects **unsatisfactory** understanding of the text. Either does not respond or talks off the topic.
1 Reflects **limited** understanding of the text. Mentions a few facts or ideas but does not express the important information or ideas.
2 Reflects **satisfactory** understanding of the text. Includes important information and ideas but neglects other key understandings.
3 Reflects **excellent** understanding of the text. Includes almost all important information and main ideas.

Key Understandings	Prompts	Score
Within the Text Recounts the most important story events, such as: April was reading to her dog; she wanted her favorite author to write a story about Golden Boy; she wrote a letter to Julia Reed (or the author) and got one back; April started to write her own story. *Note any additional understandings:*	What happened in this story? Then what happened? What happened at the end?	0 1 2 3
Beyond the Text April likes to read and write. She likes authors and stories. She likes her dog. She loved her dog, Golden Boy, so she wanted a book written about him. April learned that when you write about a dog, you have to know the dog. She learned that she could write the book about her dog and be a good author. *Note any additional understandings:*	Tell what you learned about April. What does she like to do? Why did April want her favorite author to write a story about Golden Boy? April learned a lesson about being an author. What do you think she learned?	0 1 2 3
About the Text In this book there are letters from people, a story, and a page from a book. April wrote a good letter to the author (and tells why the letter was good.) The letter she got from Julia Reed is probably what an author would really say. *Note any additional understandings:*	This book had different kinds of writing in it, didn't it? What were the different kinds of writing? Did you think April wrote a good letter to Julia Reed? Why (not)? Do you think what happened in *Dog Stories* could really happen? Why (not)?	0 1 2 3

Guide to Total Score
9–10 Excellent Comprehension
7–8 Satisfactory Comprehension
5–6 Limited Comprehension
0–4 Unsatisfactory Comprehension

Subtotal Score: _____ /9

Add 1 for any additional understandings: _____ /1

Total Score: _____ /10

Recording Forms

Part Three: Writing About Reading *(optional)*

Read the writing/drawing prompt below to the student. You can also cut the prompt on the dotted line and give it to the child. Specify the amount of time for the student to complete the task on a separate sheet of paper. (See *Assessment Guide* for more information.)

Writing About Reading Scoring Key

0 Reflects **no** understanding of the text.

1 Reflects **very limited** understanding of the text.

2 Reflects **partial** understanding of the text.

3 Reflects **excellent** understanding of the text.

— —

Write about April and what she learned in the story. You can draw a picture to go with your writing.

Recording Forms

Student _____   Grade _____   Date _____

Teacher _____   School _____

Recording Form
Part One: Oral Reading

Place the book in front of the student. Read the title and introduction.

Introduction: In this book, you will learn many things about whales, such as what
they look like, how they live, how they are born, and where you can
see them. Read to learn about the largest animals in the world.

Summary of Scores:	
Accuracy	_____
Self-correction	_____
Fluency	_____
Comprehension	_____
Writing	_____

Sources of Information Used

Page	Start Time _____ min. _____ sec. *Giants of the Sea* Level L, RW: 276, E: 16	E	SC	E			SC		
				M	S	V	M	S	V
2	The Largest Animal Think of the biggest animal you know. Is it a horse? Is it an elephant? The largest animal lives in the sea. It is much bigger than a horse or an elephant. It is the blue whale, a giant of the sea.								
3	The blue whale is the largest animal on Earth.								
4	Other whales are big, too. They may be different colors and different shapes, but they are all very large.								
	Subtotal								

Recording Forms

Part One: Oral Reading *continued*

Sources of Information Used

Page	Text	E	SC	E			SC		
				M	S	V	M	S	V
6	Breathing and Diving Whales look like fish, but they are not fish. Whales live in the water, but they cannot breathe underwater the way fish can. All whales breathe air.								
7	Whales have lungs, like you do. You breathe through your nose or mouth. Whales breathe through holes on the tops of their heads. The holes are called *blowholes*.								
8	A whale swims up to the top of the water. It blows air out of its blowhole. The whale blows so hard that it makes a cloudy spray called *blow*.								
9	Then the whale takes a deep breath. Air goes in through the blowhole. The blowhole snaps shut, and the whale is								
	Subtotal								

Recording Forms

Part One: Oral Reading *continued*

Sources of Information Used

Page	Text	E	SC	E			SC		
				M	S	V	M	S	V
9 *cont.*	ready to dive under the water again. Some whales can stay underwater for one hour or more.								
10	Baby Whales A baby whale is called a *calf*. As soon as a calf is born, the mother whale helps it swim up to the surface of the water. Then the newborn calf takes its first breath.								
11	A baby whale learns to swim soon after it is born. The calf stays close to its mother for about a year. A whale calf grows fast. A baby blue whale can gain as much as 200 pounds a day!								
	Subtotal								
	End Time _____ min. _____ sec. Total								

Have the student finish reading the book silently.

© 2011, 2008 by Irene C. Fountas and Gay Su Pinnell. Portsmouth, NH: Heinemann. This page may be photocopied.

Accuracy Rate	**Errors**	**16 or more**	**13–15**	**11–12**	**8–10**	**5–7**	**1–4**	**0**
	%	Below 95%	95%	96%	97%	98%	99%	100%

Self-Corrections _____

Fluency Score 0 1 2 3

Fluency Scoring Key

0 Reads primarily word-by-word with occasional but infrequent or inappropriate phrasing; no smooth or expressive interpretation, irregular pausing, and no attention to author's meaning or punctuation; no stress or inappropriate stress, and slow rate.

1 Reads primarily in two-word phrases with some three- and four-word groups and some word-by-word reading; almost no smooth, expressive interpretation or pausing guided by author's meaning and punctuation; almost no stress or inappropriate stress, with slow rate most of the time.

2 Reads primarily in three- or four-word phrase groups; some smooth, expressive interpretation and pausing guided by author's meaning and punctuation; mostly appropriate stress and rate with some slowdowns.

3 Reads primarily in larger, meaningful phrases or word groups; mostly smooth, expressive interpretation and pausing guided by author's meaning and punctuation; appropriate stress and rate with only a few slowdowns.

Reading Rate
(Optional)

End Time   ____ min. ____ sec.

Start Time   ____ min. ____ sec.

Total Time   ____ min. ____ sec.

Total Seconds   _____

(RW × 60) : Total Seconds = Words Per Minute (WPM)

16,560 ÷ _____ = _____ WPM

Part Two: Comprehension Conversation

Have a conversation with the student, noting the key understandings the student expresses. Use prompts as needed to stimulate discussion of understandings the student does not express. It is not necessary to use every prompt for each book. Score for evidence of all understandings expressed–with or without a prompt. Circle the number in the score column that reflects the level of understanding demonstrated.

Teacher: Talk about what you learned in this book.

<table>
<tr><td colspan="2">

Comprehension Scoring Key

0   Reflects **unsatisfactory** understanding of the text. Either does not respond or talks off the topic.

1   Reflects **limited** understanding of the text. Mentions a few facts or ideas but does not express the important information or ideas.

2   Reflects **satisfactory** understanding of the text. Includes important information and ideas but neglects other key understandings.

3   Reflects **excellent** understanding of the text. Includes almost all important information and main ideas.
</td></tr>
</table>

Key Understandings	Prompts	Score
Within the Text There are many different kinds of whales. Lists 4–5 facts about whales, such as: whales are the biggest animals; there are different kinds and sizes of whales; whales live in the water; whales breathe air; a baby whale is called a calf; whales make different sounds to communicate with each other; you can see whales at a sea park or in the sea. Describes a graphic and interprets it. *Note any additional understandings:*	What were some of the important facts about whales that were in this book? What are other facts that you learned? *Text Feature Probe* Look at the photograph and drawing on pages 2 and 3. What did you learn from these pages?	0 1 2 3
Beyond the Text Whales are like people and land animals because they breathe air. Whales make sounds to communicate with each other. I learned that (2–3 kinds of information new to the reader). *Note any additional understandings:*	How are whales like people and how are they different? Why do whales make sounds? What did you learn that was new information to you?	0 1 2 3
About the Text The author tells information in the pictures, in the paragraphs (or book), and in the charts. The writing in this book is interesting because (gives any plausible reason). The author showed pictures of horses, elephants, and whales to compare the size. And, the author said the whale is the biggest animal in the world. *Note any additional understandings:*	Why do you think the author included photographs and drawings in the book? Can you give me an example? What did the author do to make whales interesting to read about? Some whales are really big. What did the author of this book do to help us know just how big they are?	0 1 2 3

Guide to Total Score

9–10 Excellent Comprehension

7–8 Satisfactory Comprehension

5–6 Limited Comprehension

0–4 Unsatisfactory Comprehension

Subtotal Score: _____ /9

Add 1 for any additional understandings: _____ /1

Total Score: _____ /10

Part Three: Writing About Reading *(optional)*

Read the writing/drawing prompt below to the student. You can also cut the prompt on the dotted line and give it to the child. Specify the amount of time for the student to complete the task on a separate sheet of paper. (See *Assessment Guide* for more information.)

Writing About Reading Scoring Key

0 Reflects **no** understanding of the text.

1 Reflects **very limited** understanding of the text.

2 Reflects **partial** understanding of the text.

3 Reflects **excellent** understanding of the text.

— —

Write about five interesting things you learned about whales. You can draw a picture to go with your writing.

Student _____ Grade _____ Date _____

Teacher _____ School _____

Recording Form
Part One: Oral Reading

Place the book in front of the student. Read the title and introduction.

Introduction: A girl named Hanna is tired of her younger brother Nathan so she trades him for her friend Jerry's little brother William for the day. Read to find out what happened.

Summary of Scores:	
Accuracy	_____
Self-correction	_____
Fluency	_____
Comprehension	_____
Writing	_____

Sources of Information Used

Page	Start Time ____ min. ____ sec. *The Thing About Nathan* Level M, RW: 266, E: 15	E	SC	E M	E S	E V	SC M	SC S	SC V
2	"My little brother drives me crazy," said Hanna. "He is so messy! Nathan doesn't eat food. He wears it. And you wouldn't believe his room!" Hanna rolled her eyes. "It looks like a herd of cattle lives there."								
3	"My brother is a neat freak," said Jerry. "William puts all his stuff away on a shelf in his room, with everything in perfect order, like the books in the library. And you'd better not touch anything."								
4	"I'd trade my messy brother for your neat one any day," said Hanna. "This Saturday, my parents are building a rock								
	Subtotal								

Part One: Oral Reading *continued*

Sources of Information Used

Page	Text	E	SC	E			SC		
				M	S	V	M	S	V
4 *cont.*	garden in the backyard. I'm supposed to keep Nathan busy. I know I'll go nuts." "Can Nathan swim?" Jerry asked. "He swims like a fish," said Hanna. "He could come with us on Saturday," Jerry suggested. "My family is going to the city pool. William doesn't really enjoy swimming. He'd rather stay home and work on his models."								
5	"If you take Nathan swimming," said Hanna, "I'll ask my mom if William can come to our house. He can work on his models or do whatever he wants." "It's a deal!" shouted Jerry.								
	Subtotal								

Part One: Oral Reading *continued*

Sources of Information Used

Page	Text	E	SC	E			SC		
				M	S	V	M	S	V
6	Saturday morning, Jerry's parents picked up Nathan and dropped off William. Nathan ran off with just his swimsuit and flip-flops. William brought a backpack bursting with stuff. He brought a toothbrush and toothpaste. "I always brush after I eat," he said. He brought a clean shirt. "I might spill something on this one." And he brought two model kits and two videos. "We have videos you can watch," said Hanna. "I like my own, thanks," said William.								
	Subtotal								
	End Time ____ min. ____ sec. **Total**								

Have the student finish reading the book silently.

Recording Forms

Accuracy Rate	Errors	15 or more	12–14	10–11	7–9	5–6	1–4	0
	%	Below 95%	95%	96%	97%	98%	99%	100%

Self-Corrections   _____

Fluency Score   0   1   2   3

Fluency Scoring Key

0 Reads primarily word-by-word with occasional but infrequent or inappropriate phrasing; no smooth or expressive interpretation, irregular pausing, and no attention to author's meaning or punctuation; no stress or inappropriate stress, and slow rate.

1 Reads primarily in two-word phrases with some three- and four-word groups and some word-by-word reading; almost no smooth, expressive interpretation or pausing guided by author's meaning and punctuation; almost no stress or inappropriate stress, with slow rate most of the time.

2 Reads primarily in three- or four-word phrase groups; some smooth, expressive interpretation and pausing guided by author's meaning and punctuation; mostly appropriate stress and rate with some slowdowns.

3 Reads primarily in larger, meaningful phrases or word groups; mostly smooth, expressive interpretation and pausing guided by author's meaning and punctuation; appropriate stress and rate with only a few slowdowns.

Reading Rate
(Optional)

End Time   _____ min. _____ sec.

Start Time   _____ min. _____ sec.

Total Time   _____ min. _____ sec.

Total Seconds   _____

(RW × 60) ÷ Total Seconds = Words Per Minute (WPM)

15,960 ÷ _____ = _____ WPM

Part Two: Comprehension Conversation

Have a conversation with the student, noting the key understandings the student expresses. Use prompts as needed to stimulate discussion of understandings the student does not express. It is not necessary to use every prompt for each book. Score for evidence of all understandings expressed—with or without a prompt. Circle the number in the score column that reflects the level of understanding demonstrated.

Teacher: Talk about what happened in this story.

<table>
<tr><td colspan="2">Comprehension Scoring Key</td></tr>
<tr><td>0</td><td>Reflects unsatisfactory understanding of the text. Either does not respond or talks off the topic.</td></tr>
<tr><td>1</td><td>Reflects limited understanding of the text. Mentions a few facts or ideas but does not express the important information or ideas.</td></tr>
<tr><td>2</td><td>Reflects satisfactory understanding of the text. Includes important information and ideas but neglects other key understandings.</td></tr>
<tr><td>3</td><td>Reflects excellent understanding of the text. Includes almost all important information and main ideas.</td></tr>
</table>

Key Understandings	Prompts	Score
Within the Text Recounts most of the events of the story, such as: Hanna wanted to get rid of her little brother Nathan; she decided to trade him for her friend Jerry's little brother William for the day; she had a problem because William was different from Nathan (gives an example: fussy, picky eater, no fun); Hanna gave Nathan a big hug when he came back. *Note any additional understandings:*	What was the problem in this story? How did Hanna try to solve the problem? What happened after they traded brothers? How did the story end?	0 1 2 3
Beyond the Text Hanna's little brother drove her crazy because (gives a plausible reason). Hanna started to get annoyed with William. Hanna began to realize that she liked Nathan compared to William. Hanna was surprised to find that she missed Nathan after all. *Note any additional understandings:*	How did Hanna feel about Nathan at the beginning of the story? How did Hanna feel about William? How did Hanna's feelings toward Nathan change and why? What was surprising to her after they traded brothers?	0 1 2 3
About the Text Hanna started to change her mind about Nathan after being with William. You could tell what Nathan was like by what Hanna was saying and thinking about him and William. This story had a lesson (seeing someone else's brother helped her realize she really liked her own brother or that her brother wasn't so bad after all). *Note any additional understandings*	When did Hanna start to change her mind about Nathan? How did the author show what Nathan was like even though he wasn't in the story most of the time? The author was showing how Hanna learned a lesson. What was the important lesson Hanna learned?	0 1 2 3

Guide to Total Score

9–10 Excellent Comprehension

7–8 Satisfactory Comprehension

5–6 Limited Comprehension

0–4 Unsatisfactory Comprehension

Subtotal Score: _____ /9

Add 1 for any additional understandings: _____ /1

Total Score: _____ /10

Part Three: Writing About Reading *(optional)*

Read the writing/drawing prompt below to the student. You can also cut the prompt on the dotted line and give it to the child. Specify the amount of time for the student to complete the task on a separate sheet of paper. (See *Assessment Guide* for more information.)

Writing About Reading Scoring Key

0 Reflects **no** understanding of the text.

1 Reflects **very limited** understanding of the text.

2 Reflects **partial** understanding of the text.

3 Reflects **excellent** understanding of the text.

— —

Think about Hanna's point of view. Write about three of William's behaviors that are annoying. Compare them to Nathan's. You can draw a picture to go with your writing.

Student _____ Grade _____ Date _____

Teacher _____ School _____

Recording Form

Part One: Oral Reading

Place the book in front of the student. Read the title and introduction.

Introduction: In this book, you will learn how a monarch butterfly changes from an egg to a caterpillar. Read to find out how it turns its skin into a chrysalis and comes out as a butterfly.

Summary of Scores:

Accuracy	_____
Self-correction	_____
Fluency	_____
Comprehension	_____
Writing	_____

Sources of Information Used

Page	Start Time ____ min. ____ sec. *The Life of a Monarch Butterfly* Level M, RW: 225, E: 13	E	SC	E M	E S	E V	SC M	SC S	SC V
2	Do you see the speck on this leaf? It's a tiny egg! A monarch butterfly laid the egg. Someday, after many changes have taken place, the egg will become a beautiful butterfly.								
3	Egg Every butterfly starts out as an egg. The female butterfly looks for a good place to lay her eggs. Monarch butterflies lay their eggs on milkweed plants.								
	Subtotal								

Part One: Oral Reading *continued*

Sources of Information Used

Page	Text	E	SC	E			SC		
				M	S	V	M	S	V
4	Caterpillar The eggs hatch after a few days. You might be expecting a tiny butterfly. But instead, a tiny caterpillar crawls out of each egg. A newborn caterpillar is so small you can hardly see it. But it will not stay small very long. As soon as the caterpillar hatches, it starts to eat.								
5	First the newborn caterpillar eats its own eggshell. Then it starts to eat the milkweed plant. It crunches and munches like an eating machine! The caterpillar eats and eats and eats. The more it eats, the larger it								
	Subtotal								

Recording Forms

Part One: Oral Reading *continued*

Sources of Information Used

Page	Text	E	SC	E M	E S	E V	SC M	SC S	SC V
5 *cont.*	grows. The caterpillar's skin starts to get tight, like a pair of pants that are too small.								
6	Soon the caterpillar's old skin splits open! But the caterpillar has been growing a new, larger skin underneath the old skin. When the old skin breaks, the caterpillar crawls right out of it. This happens again and again. Because it grows so fast, the caterpillar will change its skin five times before it is fully grown.								
	Subtotal								
	End Time ____ min. ____ sec. **Total**								

Have the student finish reading the book silently.

Accuracy Rate	Errors	13 or more	11–12	9–10	7–8	4–6	1–3	0
	%	Below 95%	95%	96%	97%	98%	99%	100%

Self-Corrections   _____

Fluency Score   0   1   2   3

Fluency Scoring Key

0 Reads primarily word-by-word with occasional but infrequent or inappropriate phrasing; no smooth or expressive interpretation, irregular pausing, and no attention to author's meaning or punctuation; no stress or inappropriate stress, and slow rate.

1 Reads primarily in two-word phrases with some three- and four-word groups and some word-by-word reading; almost no smooth, expressive interpretation or pausing guided by author's meaning and punctuation; almost no stress or inappropriate stress, with slow rate most of the time.

2 Reads primarily in three- or four-word phrase groups; some smooth, expressive interpretation and pausing guided by author's meaning and punctuation; mostly appropriate stress and rate with some slowdowns.

3 Reads primarily in larger, meaningful phrases or word groups; mostly smooth, expressive interpretation and pausing guided by author's meaning and punctuation; appropriate stress and rate with only a few slowdowns.

Reading Rate *(Optional)*

End Time   ____ min. ____ sec.

Start Time   ____ min. ____ sec.

Total Time   ____ min. ____ sec.

Total Seconds   _____

(RW × 60) ÷ Total Seconds = Words Per Minute (WPM)

13,500 ÷ _____ = _____ WPM

Part Two: Comprehension Conversation

Have a conversation with the student, noting the key understandings the student expresses. Use prompts as needed to stimulate discussion of understandings the student does not express. It is not necessary to use every prompt for each book. Score for evidence of all understandings expressed—with or without a prompt. Circle the number in the score column that reflects the level of understanding demonstrated.

Teacher: Talk about what you learned in this book.

Comprehension Scoring Key

0 Reflects **unsatisfactory** understanding of the text. Either does not respond or talks off the topic.

1 Reflects **limited** understanding of the text. Mentions a few facts or ideas but does not express the important information or ideas.

2 Reflects **satisfactory** understanding of the text. Includes important information and ideas but neglects other key understandings.

3 Reflects **excellent** understanding of the text. Includes almost all important information and main ideas.

Key Understandings	Prompts	Score
Within the Text Describes important parts of the butterfly's life cycle: the butterfly lays an egg; the egg hatches; a caterpillar crawls out; the caterpillar eats and eats; the caterpillar's skin gets tight and splits five times; the caterpillar hangs upside down; the caterpillar has a chrysalis; the caterpillar changes to a butterfly; the butterfly comes out; the butterfly lays eggs. *Note any additional understandings:*	Tell how an egg becomes a butterfly. What happens first? Then what happens? Then what?	0 1 2 3
Beyond the Text The egg becomes a butterfly, then the butterfly lays an egg, then the egg becomes a butterfly again. *Note any additional understandings:*	How does the life cycle of a monarch butterfly keep repeating?	0 1 2 3
About the Text The author described everything in the order it happens. The author gave information in lots of different ways, such as: headings to the sections; diagrams; photographs; captions for pictures. *Note any additional understandings:*	The author told the information in a special way to make it easy for you to understand how an egg turns into a butterfly. What did the author do? In addition to the main part of the book, what are some of the other ways the author told information about the monarch butterfly?	0 1 2 3

Guide to Total Score

9–10 Excellent Comprehension

7–8 Satisfactory Comprehension

5–6 Limited Comprehension

0–4 Unsatisfactory Comprehension

Subtotal Score: _____/9

Add 1 for any additional understandings: _____/1

Total Score: _____/10

Part Three: Writing About Reading *(optional)*

Read the writing/drawing prompt below to the student. You can also cut the prompt on the dotted line and give it to the child. Specify the amount of time for the student to complete the task on a separate sheet of paper. (See *Assessment Guide* for more information.)

Writing About Reading Scoring Key

0 Reflects **no** understanding of the text.

1 Reflects **very limited** understanding of the text.

2 Reflects **partial** understanding of the text.

3 Reflects **excellent** understanding of the text.

Write about three interesting things you learned about the life of a monarch butterfly. You can draw a picture to go with your writing.

Student _____   Grade _____   Date _____

Teacher _____   School _____

Recording Form

Part One: Oral Reading

Place the book in front of the student. Read the title and introduction.

Introduction: It was the first big snowstorm in Chicago. When Patrick Waite left school at the end of the day, the problems began. Read to find out what happened to Patrick and his family.

Summary of Scores:	
Accuracy	_____
Self-correction	_____
Fluency	_____
Comprehension	_____
Writing	_____

Sources of Information Used

Page	Start Time ____ min. ____ sec. *The Big Snow* Level N, RW: 259, E: 15	E	SC	E M	E S	E V	SC M	SC S	SC V
2	With five minutes left in the school day, not a single student in room 314 was thinking about school. Outside, snow was falling, piling up like a thick blanket on the street. It was Chicago's first big storm of the year. From Patrick Waite's seat two rows from the window, it looked like six inches had already fallen. The snowflakes were huge and fluffy. Patrick felt dizzy watching them tumble from the sky. When the bell finally rang, he hurried out the door and down the sidewalk in ankle-deep snow.								
	Subtotal								

Part One: Oral Reading *continued*

Sources of Information Used

Page	Text	E	SC	E			SC		
				M	S	V	M	S	V
3	"Looks like the number six bus is stuck!" Mr. Henry said. A stuck bus didn't matter to Patrick. His family's apartment was just five blocks from the school, and he always walked. Patrick grinned. Today, he could pretend he was hiking at the North Pole.								
4	Patrick's good mood vanished after two blocks. His feet were soaked and his face felt frozen. As he waited to cross Western Avenue, a huge snowplow rolled past. It sprayed him with snow and slush. "Thanks a lot!" Patrick yelled. The driver smiled and waved.								
	Subtotal								

Part One: Oral Reading *continued*

Sources of Information Used

Page	Text	E	SC	E			SC		
				M	S	V	M	S	V
6	It seemed to take hours to walk home. Finally, Patrick stepped into the warm lobby of his apartment building. He got the mail and rode the elevator up to the tenth floor. As he opened the door, Patrick was surprised to find the apartment empty. Where was everyone? Dad and his brothers always beat him home. Patrick shook off his soggy coat and tried to ignore the uneasy feeling growing in his stomach. Maybe he was just hungry.								
	Subtotal								
	End Time ____ min. ____ sec. **Total**								

Have the student finish reading the book silently.

Accuracy Rate	Errors	15 or more	12–14	10–11	7–9	4–6	1–3	0
	%	Below 95%	95%	96%	97%	98%	99%	100%

Self-Corrections _____

Fluency Score 0 1 2 3

Fluency Scoring Key

0   Reads primarily word-by-word with occasional but infrequent or inappropriate phrasing; no smooth or expressive interpretation, irregular pausing, and no attention to author's meaning or punctuation; no stress or inappropriate stress, and slow rate.

1   Reads primarily in two-word phrases with some three- and four-word groups and some word-by-word reading; almost no smooth, expressive interpretation or pausing guided by author's meaning and punctuation; almost no stress or inappropriate stress, with slow rate most of the time.

2   Reads primarily in three- or four-word phrase groups; some smooth, expressive interpretation and pausing guided by author's meaning and punctuation; mostly appropriate stress and rate with some slowdowns.

3   Reads primarily in larger, meaningful phrases or word groups; mostly smooth, expressive interpretation and pausing guided by author's meaning and punctuation; appropriate stress and rate with only a few slowdowns.

Reading Rate *(Optional)*

End Time   ____ min. ____ sec.
Start Time   ____ min. ____ sec.
Total Time   ____ min. ____ sec.
Total Seconds _____

(RW × 60) ÷ Total Seconds = Words Per Minute (WPM)

15,540 ÷ _____ = _____ WPM

Part Two: Comprehension Conversation

Have a conversation with the student, noting the key understandings the student expresses. Use prompts as needed to stimulate discussion of understandings the student does not express. It is not necessary to use every prompt for each book. Score for evidence of all understandings expressed—with or without a prompt. Circle the number in the score column that reflects the level of understanding demonstrated.

Teacher: Talk about what happened in this story.

<table>
<tr><td colspan="4">**Comprehension Scoring Key**</td></tr>
<tr><td>**0**</td><td colspan="3">Reflects **unsatisfactory** understanding of the text. Either does not respond or talks off the topic.</td></tr>
<tr><td>**1**</td><td colspan="3">Reflects **limited** understanding of the text. Mentions a few facts or ideas but does not express the important information or ideas.</td></tr>
<tr><td>**2**</td><td colspan="3">Reflects **satisfactory** understanding of the text. Includes important information and ideas but neglects other key understandings.</td></tr>
<tr><td>**3**</td><td colspan="3">Reflects **excellent** understanding of the text. Includes almost all important information and main ideas.</td></tr>
</table>

Key Understandings	Prompts	Score
Within the Text There was a huge snowstorm in Chicago and it was causing a lot of problems. Recounts important episodes in the sequence of events, such as: Snow is falling; Patrick struggles home and finds no one there; the lights go off; Patrick and his family solve a lot of problems; Dad is still not home; everyone finally gets home. In the end, they were okay. They were all home (or his dad was home). *Note any additional understandings:*	What was the big problem at the beginning of the story? What were some of the problems that Patrick had? How did Patrick solve the problems? How did the story end?	0 1 2 3
Beyond the Text This reminds me of when our lights went out (or provides a similar example). Patrick started to get scared when he got home and was alone. His dad was a really nice person because he was always helping people. Patrick did a good job of (gives a plausible answer). He didn't complain but just did what he needed to do. *Note any additional understandings:*	Have you ever had an experience like this? How did Patrick feel when he got home alone? What kind of person do you think Patrick's dad was? What kind of person do you think Patrick was?	0 1 2 3
About the Text The author told what Patrick was thinking to show how worried he was about the dangerous snowstorm. The author showed what kind of person Patrick was by telling everything he did. *Note any additional understandings:*	How did the author help you know this was a kind of dangerous situation? How did the author show you what kind of person Patrick was?	0 1 2 3

Guide to Total Score
9–10 Excellent Comprehension
7–8 Satisfactory Comprehension
5–6 Limited Comprehension
0–4 Unsatisfactory Comprehension

Subtotal Score: _____ /9

Add 1 for any additional understandings: _____ /1

Total Score: _____ /10

Part Three: Writing About Reading *(optional)*

Read the writing/drawing prompt below to the student. You can also cut the prompt on the dotted line and give it to the child. Specify the amount of time for the student to complete the task on a separate sheet of paper. (See *Assessment Guide* for more information.)

Writing About Reading Scoring Key
0 Reflects **no** understanding of the text.
1 Reflects **very limited** understanding of the text.
2 Reflects **partial** understanding of the text.
3 Reflects **excellent** understanding of the text.

- -

Write about Patrick's feelings and how they changed from the beginning to the middle and at the end of the story. You can draw a picture to go with your writing.

Student _____ Grade _____ Date _____

Teacher _____ School _____

Recording Form
Part One: Oral Reading

Place the book in front of the student. Read the title and introduction.

Introduction: In this book, you will learn about how caves are formed. You will read about the formations in caves—stalactites that hang from the ceiling and stalagmites that come up from the floor. Read to learn all about caves.

Summary of Scores:	
Accuracy	_____
Self-correction	_____
Fluency	_____
Comprehension	_____
Writing	_____

Sources of Information Used

Page	Start Time ____ min. ____ sec. *Exploring Caves* Level N, RW: 281, E: 16	E	SC	E M	E S	E V	SC M	SC S	SC V
2	Caves and Cavers Caves are dark, hidden worlds that some people like to explore. These people are called *cavers*. Some big caves, called *caverns*, have rooms that connect, just like a house. Cavers have fun crawling, climbing, and sliding through rocky spaces—some tiny, some huge—to learn about these interesting places.								
4	How Are Caves Formed? Scientists have different ideas about how caves are formed. Most think caves are created by water.								
	Subtotal								

Part One: Oral Reading *continued*

Page	Text	E	SC	E			SC		
				M	S	V	M	S	V
4 *cont.*	When rain falls, it mixes with an invisible gas in the air. When the water reaches the ground, it seeps into the earth.								
5	The water continues going deeper into the earth until it touches rock. Very slowly, the water eats away at the rock and causes tiny cracks to develop. The cracks in the rock grow wider with time. Then the water flows out and leaves behind a cave.								
6	Safety First Guides work at many cave sites. These experts can lead people through the twisting tunnels and paths inside caves without getting lost. Cavers love adventure, but they have to be smart and careful. One rule they								
	Subtotal								

© 2011, 2008 by Irene C. Fountas and Gay Su Pinnell. Portsmouth, NH: Heinemann. This page may be photocopied.

Sources of Information Used

Part One: Oral Reading *continued*

Sources of Information Used

Page	Text	E	SC	E			SC		
				M	S	V	M	S	V
6 *cont.*	follow is never to explore alone. There must be at least three people in a group. That way, if there's an accident, someone can go get help.								
7	Cavers follow another rule—be prepared! It can get very cold inside a cave, so cavers wear warm clothing. They also wear helmets to protect their heads from falling rocks. Sturdy hiking boots help them walk along bumpy or slippery paths.								
8	It's very dark inside a cave, but instead of carrying flashlights, many cavers wear helmets with lights attached to them. That way their hands are free to hold on as they climb on rocks.								
	Subtotal								
End Time ____ min. ____ sec.	Total								

Have the student finish reading the book silently.

Accuracy Rate	Errors	16 or more	14–15	11–13	8–10	5–7	1–4	0
	%	Below 95%	95%	96%	97%	98%	99%	100%

Self-Corrections

_____

Fluency Score   0   1   2   3

Fluency Scoring Key

0 Reads primarily word-by-word with occasional but infrequent or inappropriate phrasing; no smooth or expressive interpretation, irregular pausing, and no attention to author's meaning or punctuation; no stress or inappropriate stress, and slow rate.

1 Reads primarily in two-word phrases with some three- and four-word groups and some word-by-word reading; almost no smooth, expressive interpretation or pausing guided by author's meaning and punctuation; almost no stress or inappropriate stress, with slow rate most of the time.

2 Reads primarily in three- or four-word phrase groups; some smooth, expressive interpretation and pausing guided by author's meaning and punctuation; mostly appropriate stress and rate with some slowdowns.

3 Reads primarily in larger, meaningful phrases or word groups; mostly smooth, expressive interpretation and pausing guided by author's meaning and punctuation; appropriate stress and rate with only a few slowdowns.

Reading Rate
(Optional)

End Time   _____ min. _____ sec.

Start Time   _____ min. _____ sec.

Total Time   _____ min. _____ sec.

Total Seconds   _____

(RW × 60) ÷ Total Seconds = Words Per Minute (WPM)

16,860 ÷ _____ = _____ WPM

Part Two: Comprehension Conversation

Have a conversation with the student, noting the key understandings the student expresses. Use prompts as needed to stimulate discussion of understandings the student does not express. It is not necessary to use every prompt for each book. Score for evidence of all understandings expressed—with or without a prompt. Circle the number in the score column that reflects the level of understanding demonstrated.

Teacher: Talk about what you learned in this book.

Comprehension Scoring Key
0 Reflects **unsatisfactory** understanding of the text. Either does not respond or talks off the topic.
1 Reflects **limited** understanding of the text. Mentions a few facts or ideas but does not express the important information or ideas.
2 Reflects **satisfactory** understanding of the text. Includes important information and ideas but neglects other key understandings.
3 Reflects **excellent** understanding of the text. Includes almost all important information and main ideas.

Key Understandings	Prompts	Score
Within the Text Caves are spaces under the ground. Reports 3–4 interesting facts about caves, such as: people who like to explore caves are cavers; caves have rooms; water eats away at the rock to make a cave; three people need to go together in a cave; cavers wear warm clothes, helmets with lights, and hiking boots; animals live in caves; water drips from stalactites and stalagmites. *Note any additional understandings:*	What is a cave? What did you learn about caves? What else?	0 1 2 3
Beyond the Text Caves are very important, and we need to take care of them. Recounts one major idea from the text, such as: It takes a long time to make a cave; caves are home to many animals, so we need to take care of them; we can learn a lot about Earth from caves. I would like to explore a cave because (gives a plausible reason). *Note any additional understandings:*	What was the most important idea in this book? What did you learn about why caves are important to us? I might (or might not) like to explore a cave, would you? Why (not)?	0 1 2 3

Continued on next page.

Recording Forms

Part Two: Comprehension Conversation *continued*

Key Understandings	Prompts	Score
About the Text The author put information in the book that she thought readers would not know and would find interesting (gives examples). The author read a lot about caves to learn about them and so she could write accurately about them. The facts must be right in this book because (gives author's credentials, references, other). There are different kinds of information in different places in the book. The sections (or headings, titles, table of contents) tell you where to look. The author wants you to think that caves are very interesting and make you want to visit one or read more about them. *Note any additional understandings:*	How do you think the author decided what information to put in the book? Do you think the information in this book is accurate? Why (not)? How does the author help you find the different kinds of information in this book? What do you think the author wants you to think about caves? What do you think she might want you to do after you read this book?	0 1 2 3

Guide to Total Score

9–10 **Excellent** Comprehension

7–8 **Satisfactory** Comprehension

5–6 **Limited** Comprehension

0–4 **Unsatisfactory** Comprehension

Subtotal Score: _____ /9

Add 1 for any additional understandings: _____ /1

Total Score: _____ /10

© 2011, 2008 by Irene C. Fountas and Gay Su Pinnell. Portsmouth NH: Heinemann. This page may be photocopied.

Part Three: Writing About Reading *(optional)*

Read the writing/drawing prompt below to the student. You can also cut the prompt on the dotted line and give it to the child. Specify the amount of time for the student to complete the task on a separate sheet of paper. (See *Assessment Guide* for more information.)

Writing About Reading Scoring Key

0 Reflects **no** understanding of the text.

1 Reflects **very limited** understanding of the text.

2 Reflects **partial** understanding of the text.

3 Reflects **excellent** understanding of the text.

Write about five interesting things you learned about caves. You can draw a picture to go with your writing.

Summary Forms

The following section includes a variety of useful forms for summarizing the information from your benchmark assessment conferences. The summary forms will help you analyze an individual student's performance or the performance of your whole class. You will also find forms for constructing a graph of student progress over time. You can photocopy these forms or print them from the *Forms CD-ROM*.

Student _____ Grade _____

Teacher _____ Date _____

School _____

Benchmark Independent Level*	_____
Benchmark Instructional Level**	_____
Recommended Placement Level	_____

Assessment Summary Form   *List the titles read by the student from lowest to highest level.*

Title	System 1 or 2	Fiction/Nonfiction	Level	Accuracy	Comprehension	Independent * (check one)	Instructional ** (check one)	Hard *** (check one)	Self-Correction	Fluency Levels G–Z	Rate Levels J–Z (optional)	Writing About Reading (optional)

*Independent Level

Levels A–K: Highest level read with 95–100% accuracy and excellent or satisfactory comprehension.

Levels L–Z: Highest level read with 98–100% accuracy and excellent or satisfactory comprehension.

**Instructional Level

Levels A–K: Highest level read with 90–94% accuracy and excellent or satisfactory comprehension or 95–100% accuracy and limited comprehension.

Levels L–Z: Highest level read with 95–97% accuracy and excellent or satisfactory comprehension or 98–100% accuracy and limited comprehension.

***Hard Level

Levels A–K: Highest level read at which accuracy is below 90% with any level of comprehension.

Levels L–Z: Highest level read at which accuracy is below 95% with any level of comprehension.

Comprehension			
Levels A–K		**Levels L–Z**	
6–7	Excellent	**9–10**	Excellent
5	Satisfactory	**7–8**	Satisfactory
4	Limited	**5–6**	Limited
0–3	Unsatisfactory	**0–4**	Unsatisfactory

Behaviors and Understandings to Notice, Teach, and Support (See *The Continuum of Literacy Learning*)

Summary Forms

Student _____   Grade _____   Year _____

Teacher _____   School _____

Bi-Annual Assessment Summary

	Date _____	Date _____
Independent Level	Level _____	Level _____
Accuracy	_____ %	_____ %
Comprehension	_____ / _____	_____ / _____
Self-Correction	_____	_____
Fluency	0 1 2 3	0 1 2 3
Rate *(optional)*	_____ WPM	_____ WPM
Writing About Reading *(optional)*	0 1 2 3	0 1 2 3
Instructional Level	Level _____	Level _____
Accuracy	_____ %	_____ %
Comprehension	_____ / _____	_____ / _____
Self-Correction	_____	_____
Fluency	0 1 2 3	0 1 2 3
Rate *(optional)*	_____ WPM	_____ WPM
Writing About Reading *(optional)*	0 1 2 3	0 1 2 3

Behaviors and Understandings to Notice, Teach, and Support

Summary Forms

Student _____   Grade _____   Year _____

Teacher _____   School _____

Tri-Annual Assessment Summary

	Date _____	Date _____	Date _____
Independent Level	Level _____	Level _____	Level _____
Accuracy	_____ %	_____ %	_____ %
Comprehension	_____ / _____	_____ / _____	_____ / _____
Self-Correction	_____	_____	_____
Fluency	0 1 2 3	0 1 2 3	0 1 2 3
Rate *(optional)*	_____ WPM	_____ WPM	_____ WPM
Writing About Reading *(optional)*	0 1 2 3	0 1 2 3	0 1 2 3
Instructional Level	Level _____	Level _____	Level _____
Accuracy	_____ %	_____ %	_____ %
Comprehension	_____ / _____	_____ / _____	_____ / _____
Self-Correction	_____	_____	_____
Fluency	0 1 2 3	0 1 2 3	0 1 2 3
Rate *(optional)*	_____ WPM	_____ WPM	_____ WPM
Writing About Reading *(optional)*	0 1 2 3	0 1 2 3	0 1 2 3

Behaviors and Understandings to Notice, Teach, and Support

Summary Forms

Student _____   Grade _____   Year _____

Teacher _____   School _____

Quarterly Assessment Summary

	Date _____	Date _____	Date _____	Date _____
Independent Level	Level _____	Level _____	Level _____	Level _____
Accuracy	_____ %	_____ %	_____ %	_____ %
Comprehension	_____ / _____	_____ / _____	_____ / _____	_____ / _____
Self-Correction	_____	_____	_____	_____
Fluency	0 1 2 3	0 1 2 3	0 1 2 3	0 1 2 3
Rate *(optional)*	_____ WPM	_____ WPM	_____ WPM	_____ WPM
Writing About Reading *(optional)*	0 1 2 3	0 1 2 3	0 1 2 3	0 1 2 3
Instructional Level	Level _____	Level _____	Level _____	Level _____
Accuracy	_____ %	_____ %	_____ %	_____ %
Comprehension	_____ / _____	_____ / _____	_____ / _____	_____ / _____
Self-Correction	_____	_____	_____	_____
Fluency	0 1 2 3	0 1 2 3	0 1 2 3	0 1 2 3
Rate *(optional)*	_____ WPM	_____ WPM	_____ WPM	_____ WPM
Writing About Reading *(optional)*	0 1 2 3	0 1 2 3	0 1 2 3	0 1 2 3

Behaviors and Understandings to Notice, Teach, and Support

Summary Forms

Teacher _____   Grade _____   Year _____

School _____

Date _____

Class Record Form

Student Name	Benchmark Independent Level	Benchmark Instructional Level	Accur.	Comp.	Fluency	Benchmark Placement Level	Notes
1.							
2.							
3.							
4.							
5.							
6.							
7.							
8.							
9.							
10.							
11.							
12.							
13.							
14.							
15.							
16.							
17.							
18.							
19.							
20.							
21.							
22.							
23.							
24.							
25.							
26.							
27.							
28.							
29.							
30.							

Summary Forms

Student _____   Grade _____

Teacher _____   School _____

Annual Record of Reading Progress

Record the title and accuracy rate. Draw a circle to indicate text level.

● = below 90% (Levels A–K) or below 95% (Levels L–Z)   ○ = 90% or above (Levels A–K) or 95% or above (Levels L–Z)

Title /Accuracy Rate																				

Book Level																					
System 2	Z																				
	Y																				
	X																				
	W																				
	V																				
	U																				
	T																				
	S																				
	R																				
	Q																				
	P																				
	O																				
	N																				
	M																				
	L																				
System 1	N																				
	M																				
	L																				
	K																				
	J																				
	I																				
	H																				
	G																				
	F																				
	E																				
	D																				
	C																				
	B																				
	A																				
Date																					

Longitudinal Record of Reading Progress

Student _____ School _____

Record the date and draw a circle in the box to indicate student's level. Check one: _____ Benchmark Independent Level _____ Benchmark Instructional Level

Level Benchmark Title																																					
Z ☐ Train at the Top																																					
☐ Surviving the Blitz																																					
Y ☐ Int'l Space Station																																					
☐ Saying Goodbye																																					
X ☐ The Internet																																					
☐ A Weighty Decision																																					
W ☐ Coretta Scott King																																					
☐ Summer Vacation																																					
V ☐ Tsunamis																																					
☐ A Call for Change																																					
U ☐ Earthquakes																																					
☐ Canyon Mystery																																					
T ☐ Wolves Howl																																					
☐ "Get a Horse!"																																					
S ☐ Animal Adaptations																																					
☐ Could Be Worse																																					
R ☐ Fishing Smarts																																					
☐ The Election																																					
Q ☐ Polar Bear																																					
☐ A Secret Home																																					
P ☐ Animal Instincts																																					
☐ Plenty of Pets																																					
O ☐ Snake Myths																																					
☐ The New Girl																																					
N ☐ Dogs at Work																																					
☐ Vanessa's Butterfly																																					
M ☐ City Hawks																																					
☐ Saving Up																																					
L ☐ Baby Monkey																																					
☐ Ernie Learns																																					
N ☐ Exploring Caves																																					
☐ The Big Snow																																					
M ☐ Monarch Butterfly																																					
☐ Thing About Nathan																																					
L ☐ Giants of the Sea																																					
☐ Dog Stories																																					
K ☐ Animal Senses																																					
☐ Edwin's Haircut																																					
J ☐ More Than a Pet																																					
☐ Our New Neighbors																																					
I ☐ All About Koalas																																					
☐ The Best Cat																																					
H ☐ Trucks																																					
☐ The Sleepover Party																																					
G ☐ Bubbles																																					
☐ Bedtime for Nick																																					
F ☐ From Nest to Bird																																					
☐ Anna's New Glasses																																					
E ☐ The Zoo																																					
☐ The Loose Tooth																																					
D ☐ Mr. Brown																																					
☐ Nice Little House																																					
C ☐ Shopping																																					
☐ Socks																																					
B ☐ Playing																																					
☐ My Little Dog																																					
A ☐ At the Park																																					
☐ Best Friends																																					
Date																																					
Grade	K		1		2		3		4		5		6		7		8																				

System 2 (levels L–Z), *System 1* (levels A–N)

Summary Forms

Student _____ Grade _____ Date _____

Teacher _____ School _____

Optional Assessment Summary Form

Choose from the optional assessments to diagnose the skills of individual students, as needed. Using the chart below, record each student's score next to the chosen assessment.

Assessment	Date	Date	Date	Date
Letter Recognition				
Early Literacy Behaviors				
Reading HF Words (25)				
Reading HF Words (50)				
Reading HF Words (100)				
Reading HF Words (200)				
Phonological Awareness (Initial)				
Phonological Awareness (Blending)				
Phonological Awareness (Segmenting)				
Phonological Awareness (Rhyming)				
Word Writing				
Writing Picture Names				
Phonograms				
Consonant Blends				
Vowel Clusters				
Suffixes				
Compound Words				
One- and Two-Syllable Words				
Syllables in Longer Words				
Concept Words (Number)				
Concept Words (Color)				
Synonyms				
Antonyms				
Homophones				
Vocabulary in Context A				
Vocabulary in Context B				
Vocabulary in Context C				
Vocabulary in Context D				
Vocabulary in Context E				
Vocabulary in Context F				
Vocabulary in Context G				
Vocabulary in Context H				
Vocabulary in Context I				
Vocabulary in Context J				
Vocabulary in Context K				
Vocabulary in Context L				
Vocabulary in Context M				
Vocabulary in Context N				

Optional Assessments

The following section includes a variety of useful assessments for the diagnosis of strengths and needs of individuals, small groups, or your whole class. Some of these optional assessments may be required at particular grade levels by your school system. You can photocopy the assessments from this book or print them from the *Forms CD-ROM*.

Criteria for evaluating students' performance on the optional assessments can be found in Appendix C of the *Assessment Guide.*

Getting Started

In this section, you will find tools to help you determine the starting point for a benchmark assessment conference when you do not have other information such as previous reading records, to help you make a good decision.

Where-to-Start Word Test

Description   Students read a leveled word list.

You Need
▶ The Where-to-Start Word List

▶ The Where-to-Start Chart to determine the level at which to start Benchmark Assessment

▶ Where-to-Start Individual Record form

Why Use It   If you do not have or are not confident about reading performance information about a child, this quick assessment will give you a broad notion of the level at which to begin Benchmark Assessment.

How to Use It
▶ Ask the student to read the list for the level below his/her grade level (e.g., kindergarteners and first graders should begin with the **Beginning** list, second graders with **List 1**, fourth graders with **List 3**, etc.).

▶ *"I want you to read some words. When you come to a hard word, try it. If you cannot read it, go on to the next word. I'll be making notes while you read. Start here."*

▶ Place a card under the first word in the appropriate word list. Have the child move the card down the list as he reads. If the student spends too much time on a word (more than 5 seconds), say *"Read the next one."*

▶ As the student reads, score and record word reading on a copy of the list:

1. Check each word read accurately, including correct guesses, self-corrected readings, and accepted local variations in pronunciation.
2. Write incorrect responses next to each word. If word not attempted, leave the space blank.
3. Score as errors words that the student
   • cannot read
   • substitutes with another word or other sounds
   • says several different ways and is uncertain of the correct pronunciation
   • reads incompletely (*bed* instead of *beds*) or adds sounds to (*plays* instead of *play*)
4. Do not prompt, coach, or ask the student to repeat a word (unless you could not hear it).
5. Record the number of words read accurately at the bottom of each list.

If the child reads 19 to 20 words on a list correctly, then go to the next list. If a child reads less than 18 words correctly, then stop and begin the text reading at the appropriate level shown on the chart below.

Where-to-Start Chart

Number Correct	Beginning List	List 1	List 2	List 3	List 4
0–5	A	A	E	I	M
6–10	A	B	F	J	M
11–15	A	C	G	K	N
16–18	B	D	H	L	N
19–20	Go to List 1	Go to List 2	Go to List 3	Go to List 4	N

Beginning Word List

me	mom
I	the
can	and
to	he
my	look
we	is
in	see
like	come
it	get
up	at

Getting Started

Word List 1

jump	play
here	was
little	bike
went	with
has	they
girl	this
will	bed
have	feet
ball	one
make	said

Word List 2

want	morning
friend	three
puppy	cool
basket	drop
could	grass
dark	when
down	first
road	train
plant	queen
away	scream

Getting Started

Word List 3

plate	forest
year	once
noise	scramble
under	again
twisted	careful
giant	breakfast
knives	batter
what	suddenly
around	badge
because	village

Word List 4

silence	plastic
serious	ocean
nature	perform
station	delicious
graceful	pebble
heavy	understood
against	destiny
excuse	future
traffic	anger
reward	honey

© 2011, 2008 by Irene C. Fountas and Gay Su Pinnell. Portsmouth, NH: Heinemann. This page may be photocopied.

Getting Started

Where-to-Start Word Test—Individual Record

Name _____   Date _____

Beginning		List 1		List 2	
me		jump		want	
I		here		friend	
can		little		puppy	
to		went		basket	
my		has		could	
we		girl		dark	
in		will		down	
like		have		road	
it		ball		plant	
up		make		away	
mom		play		morning	
the		was		three	
and		bike		cool	
he		with		drop	
look		they		grass	
is		this		when	
see		bed		first	
come		feet		train	
get		one		queen	
at		said		scream	
	/20		/20		/20

Getting Started

Where-to-Start Word Test—Individual Record

Name _____ Date _____

List 3		List 4	
plate		silence	
year		serious	
noise		nature	
under		station	
twisted		graceful	
giant		heavy	
knives		against	
what		excuse	
around		traffic	
because		reward	
forest		plastic	
once		ocean	
scramble		perform	
again		delicious	
careful		pebble	
breakfast		understood	
batter		destiny	
suddenly		future	
badge		anger	
village		honey	
	/20		**/20**

Getting Started

Reading Interview

Description ▶ Children answer questions about their reading attitudes, interests, and habits.

You Need ▶ Reading Interview sheet

Why Use It
This assessment will help you learn about children's reading interests; you can use it to help them find titles they'll be interested in reading. It will also serve as a guide to how aware they are of their reading strengths and weaknesses. By looking at the interviews across the entire class, you can gauge which reading experiences would be appropriate for the whole group, and which would be more appropriate for a small group or an individual.

How to Use It ▶ Administer this assessment individually by asking each question and recording the child's responses.

▶ You may administer the assessment to the class by giving each child a copy of the Reading Interview sheet (as appropriate to the grade level). If necessary, read each question aloud. Provide ample time for children to write their responses.

▶ If the assessment is administered to the whole class, you may wish to meet with children individually to discuss their responses.

What to Notice ▶ Whether children have a difficult time thinking of books they enjoy

▶ Breadth and width of children's reading experiences, including variety of topics, genres, and authors

▶ Level of awareness of reading strengths and weaknesses

Reading Interview Sheet

Student _____   Grade _____   Date _____

Teacher _____

Answer each question.

1. How many books did you read last year or so far this year? _____

    _____

2. What are the different kinds of books you have read? (Genres: realistic fiction, fantasy, biography and autobiography, historical fiction, informational books, articles)_____

    _____

    _____

    _____

    _____

3. What are your favorite genres to read? _____

    _____

    _____

    _____

4. Which were the best books you read last year or so far this year? What made these books good? _____

    _____

    _____

    _____

    _____

    _____

5. Who are two of your favorite authors and why do you like them?_____

    _____

    _____

    _____

    _____

    _____

Getting Started

6. What is your favorite poem? Why do you like it? _____
    _____
    _____
    _____
    _____
    _____

7. What do you know how to do well as a reader? What could you do better?_____
    _____
    _____
    _____
    _____
    _____

8. What have you learned as a reader that makes you proud? _____
    _____
    _____
    _____
    _____
    _____

9. What have you learned about reading fiction books? _____
    _____
    _____
    _____
    _____
    _____

10. What have you learned about reading nonfiction books? _____
    _____
    _____
    _____
    _____
    _____

Teacher's Comments:_____
_____
_____

Assessing Fluency and Phrasing

In this section, you will find a detailed rubric for assessing the multiple dimensions of fluent and phrased reading. Although the Recording Form provides a four-point fluency rubric, you may want to use this rubric to analyze specific aspects of fluency for particular students. You will find practice examples for evaluating fluency on the *Professional Development DVD*.

Six Dimensions Fluency Rubric

Description   Use this form to observe and record a student's oral reading of a Benchmark book or other leveled texts.

You Need   ▶ A Benchmark or other book at an appropriate level

▶ The Six Dimensions Fluency Rubric

Why Use It   The fluency assessment helps you notice and think about the dimensions of oral reading that a student controls and needs to develop.

How to Use It   ▶ Administer this assessment individually.

▶ Have the student read aloud the selected text.

▶ Consider rate, phrasing, pausing, intonation, and stress as separate dimensions and rate each of them from 0 to 3 on the rubric.

▶ Then rate integration, your overall impression of the student's orchestration of all the elements in the reading.

What to Notice   ▶ Dimensions of fluency the reader is demonstrating and those neglected

Student _____   Date _____

Six Dimensions Fluency Rubric

1. Pausing Pausing refers to the way the reader's voice is guided by punctuation (for example, short breath at a comma; full stop with voice going down at periods and up at question marks; full stop at dashes).

0	1	2	3
Almost no pausing to reflect punctuation or meaning of the text *Needs intensive teaching and/ or text not appropriate*	Some pausing to reflect the punctuation and meaning of the text *Needs explicit teaching, prompting, and reinforcing*	Most of the reading evidences appropriate pausing to reflect the punctuation and meaning of the text. *Needs some prompting and reinforcing*	Almost all the reading is characterized by pausing to reflect punctuation and meaning of the text. *Teaching not needed*

2. Phrasing Phrasing refers to the way readers put words together in groups to represent the meaningful units of language. Sometimes phrases are cued by punctuation such as commas, but often they are not. Phrased reading sounds like oral language, though more formal.

0	1	2	3
No evidence of appropriate phrasing during the reading *Needs intensive teaching and/ or text not appropriate*	Some evidence of appropriate phrasing during the reading *Needs explicit teaching, prompting, and reinforcing*	Much of the reading evidences appropriate phrasing. *Needs some prompting and reinforcing*	Almost all the reading is appropriately phrased. *Teaching not needed*

3. Stress Stress refers to the emphasis readers place on particular words (louder tone) to reflect the meaning as speakers would do in oral language.

0	1	2	3
Almost no stress on appropriate words to reflect the meaning of the text *Needs intensive teaching and/ or text not appropriate*	Some stress on appropriate words to reflect the meaning of the text *Needs explicit teaching, prompting, and reinforcing*	Most of the reading evidences stress on appropriate words to reflect the meaning of the text. *Needs some prompting and reinforcing*	Almost all of the reading is characterized by stress on appropriate words to reflect the meaning of the text. *Teaching not needed*

4. Intonation Intonation refers to the way the reader varies the voice in tone, pitch, and volume to reflect the meaning of the text—sometimes called expression.

0	1	2	3
Almost no variation in voice or tone (pitch) to reflect the meaning of the text *Needs intensive teaching and/ or text not appropriate*	Some evidence of variation in voice or tone (pitch) to reflect the meaning of the text *Needs explicit teaching, prompting, and reinforcing*	Most of the reading evidences variation in voice or tone (pitch) to reflect the meaning of the text. *Needs some prompting and reinforcing*	Almost all of the reading evidences variation in voice or tone (pitch) to reflect the meaning of the text. *Teaching not needed*

5. Rate Rate refers to the pace at which a reader moves through the text—not too fast and not too slow. The reader moves along steadily with few slow-downs, stops, or pauses to solve words. If the reader has only a few short pauses for word solving and picks up the pace again, look at the overall rate.

0	1	2	3
Almost no evidence of appropriate rate during the reading *Needs intensive teaching and/ or text not appropriate*	Some evidence of appropriate rate during the reading *Needs explicit teaching, prompting, and reinforcing*	Most of the reading evidences appropriate rate. *Needs some prompting and reinforcing*	Almost all of the reading evidences appropriate rate. *Teaching not needed*

6. Integration Integration involves the way a reader consistently and evenly orchestrates rate, phrasing, pausing, intonation, and stress.

0	1	2	3
Almost none of the reading is fluent. *Needs intensive teaching and/ or text not appropriate*	Some of the reading is fluent. *Needs explicit teaching, prompting, and reinforcing*	Most of the reading is fluent. *Needs some prompting and reinforcing*	Almost all of the reading is fluent. *Teaching not needed*

Guiding Principles for Rating Try to focus on one aspect at a time but give your overall impression.

© 2011, 2008 by Irene C. Fountas and Gay Su Pinnell. Portsmouth, NH: Heinemann. This page may be photocopied.

Assessing Fluency and Phrasing

Phonics and Word Analysis Assessments

You can select from the following individual, small group, or whole class assessments to identify strengths and needs in your students' knowledge of letter-sound relationships and in their ability to take words apart. You will also find a variety of forms to help you summarize and analyze the results. Use this information in conjunction with the data you gather in the benchmark assessment conferences.

Letter Recognition: **Uppercase and Lowercase Naming**

Description   Children say the names of the alphabet by recognizing the shapes of uppercase and lowercase letters.

You Need
- Uppercase Letter Recognition Sheet
- Lowercase Letter Recognition Sheet
- Letter Recognition Assessment—Individual Record form
- Letter Recognition Assessment—Class Record form

Why Use It   This assessment will identify letter forms children can associate with the corresponding letter name. Use this information to plan lessons on letters and also to decide what letters and letter features to bring to children's attention during interactive writing or shared reading.

How to Use It
- Administer this assessment individually. Start with uppercase letters and then assess lowercase letters.
- Give the child the Uppercase Letter Recognition Sheet. Cover all but the top row. Point to each letter in the top row and ask the child "What's this?" Once the child understands, have the child continue reading across as you move down the rows. If the child pauses more than three to five seconds, tell the child to go on to the right. Repeat the process with the Lowercase Letter Recognition Sheet.
- Record responses on the child's Individual Record.

What to Notice
- Number of letters named accurately
- Unknown letter names
- Speed in letter recognition
- Letter confusions and substitutions
- Sounds known without knowledge of letter names

Uppercase Letter Recognition Sheet

H	E	M	T
I	P	Q	U
O	C	W	B
X	V	J	S
G	N	Y	K
Z	R	A	F
L	D		

Phonics & Word Analysis

Lowercase Letter Recognition Sheet

h	e	m	t
i	p	q	u
o	c	w	b
x	v	j	s
g	n	y	k
z	r	a	f
l	d		

Phonics & Word Analysis

Letter Recognition Assessment—**Individual Record**

Name _____ Grade _____ Date _____

Directions: Use Uppercase and Lowercase Letter Recognition Sheets. Slide a card under each letter and ask the child to read it. Check (✓) accurate responses and note substitutions. Calculate number of letters known (as well as total score). Note unknown letters. Evaluate substitutions to determine features to which children are attending.

Letter	Accurate	Substitution or Confusion
H		
E		
M		
T		
I		
P		
Q		
U		
O		
C		
W		
B		
X		
V		
J		
S		
G		
N		
Y		
K		
Z		
R		
A		
F		
L		
D		
Score		

Letter	Accurate	Substitution or Confusion
h		
e		
m		
t		
i		
p		
q		
u		
o		
c		
w		
b		
x		
v		
j		
s		
g		
n		
y		
k		
z		
r		
a		
f		
l		
d		
Score		

Unknown Letters	Substitutions	Total Score for All Letters

Phonics & Word Analysis

Letter Recognition Assessment—**Class Record**

Uppercase and Lowercase Letter Recognition Assessment—Class Record

Name	Identified 0–10 Uppercase Letters	Identified 11–15 Uppercase Letters	Identified 16–26 Uppercase Letters	Identified 0–10 Lowercase Letters	Identified 11–15 Lowercase Letters	Identified 16–26 Lowercase Letters
1.						
2.						
3.						
4.						
5.						
6.						
7.						
8.						
9.						
10.						
11.						
12.						
13.						
14.						
15.						
16.						
17.						
18.						
19.						
20.						
21.						
22.						
23.						
24.						
25.						
26.						
27.						
28.						

Early Literacy Behaviors

Description   Children demonstrate that they know and can use the following conventions related to print:

▶ Finding specific words within a text

▶ Matching words they hear with words they read

You Need   ▶ Any Level B or C book from the *Benchmark Assessment System 1*

▶ Early Literacy Behaviors Assessment—Individual Record form

▶ Early Literacy Behaviors Assessment—Class Summary form

Why Use It   This assessment will help you learn whether children can think about a specific known word and how it looks and then locate it in a text. You will also learn whether children can think about an unknown word, say it, think about the sounds and letters, and use visual features to find the word within the lines of text.

One key early behavior for the young reader to master is the coordination between spoken and written language. The reader must understand and demonstrate that one spoken word is matched with one printed word (cluster of letters defined by white space). If a child knows where to start reading (on the left) and where to go after that (returning to the left to start a new line), then some important orienting behaviors are under control. If he can point to the words while you read the story, then he is gaining control of the directional behaviors needed for reading.

You will also want to know if the reader can recognize and use letters within print. A reader may learn a letter in isolation and even connect it with a sound, but it is an additional challenge to locate letters that are embedded in print. You will want to know whether the reader can distinguish individual letters by their features and can distinguish between letters and words (clusters of letters). Finally you will learn whether a reader is beginning to notice important graphic signs such as punctuation, which help in parsing language (paragraphs into sentences and sentences into phrases).

All of these understandings are key to the reader's developing an early system for processing print, and they are foundational to taking on and understanding longer texts. The information from this added assessment will guide your teaching in ways that can help emergent readers automatically apply understandings such as left to right directionality and word by word matching.

How to Use It   ▶ Select a Level B or C book from the *Benchmark Assessment System 1* that you do not plan to use for assessment.

▶ Read the book to the child.

▶ Turn back to the front of the book and look at the second or third page. Ask:

1. Where do I start reading? [The child should point to the left margin on line 1.]

2. Where do I go after that? [The child should point to the left margin on line 2.]

3. Find [word] on this page. [Select a word that the child has recognized on the word test. If no words were recognized, skip this item.]

4. Find [word] on this page. [Have the child locate another known word. If the child does not recognize 2 words, skip this item.]

5. Say [word.] Find [word] on this page. [You may want to turn to another page. Select a word that the child did not recognize on the word test and that begins with a consonant. Have the child say it slowly and then locate it on the page.]

6. Point while I read. [Read the page, asking the child to point. The child should match one spoken word with one word in print.]

7. Find the letter _____. [Have the child locate a letter after you say it.]

8. Find the letter _____. [Have the child locate another letter after you say it.]

9. Find a word that starts with [letter.] [Using any letter, have the child locate a word that starts with it.]

10. What's this? [Point to an ending mark (period or exclamation mark). Ask the child to tell what it means.]

What to Notice As you interact with the child around a simple text, notice:

▶ behaviors that seem quick and automatic

▶ speed in locating words and letters

▶ ability to connect letters, sounds, and words

▶ ability to match one spoken word with one written word

▶ ability to distinguish letter features when they are embedded in words

▶ ability to understand the difference between letters and words

▶ ability to read left to right and return to left margin

Early Literacy Behaviors Assessment—**Individual Record**

Name _____ Grade _____ Date _____

	Question/Prompt	**Accurate Response**	**Check**
1	Where do I start reading?	Points to the left margin on line 1	
2	Where do I go after that?	Points to the left margin on line 2	
3	Find _____ on this page.	Finds a known word	
4	Find _____ on this page.	Finds a known word	
5	Say _____ . Find _____ on this page.	Finds an unknown word after saying it	
6	Point while I read.	Points, matching word by word, while you read two to four lines of print	
7	Find the letter _____.	Finds the letter that you say	
8	Find the letter _____.	Finds the letter that you say	
9	Find a word that starts with _____.	Finds a word that starts with the letter that you say	
10	What's this?	Finds an ending mark, either period, question mark, or exclamation point	
		TOTAL POINTS	

Phonics & Word Analysis

Early Literacy Behaviors Assessment—**Class Summary**

Name	Total Points	Notes
1.		
2.		
3.		
4.		
5.		
6.		
7.		
8.		
9.		
10.		
11.		
12.		
13.		
14.		
15.		
16.		
17.		
18.		
19.		
20.		
21.		
22.		
23.		
24.		
25.		
26.		
27.		
28.		

Phonics & Word Analysis

Reading High-Frequency Words: **25 Words**

Description   Children read 25 high-frequency words.

You Need
▶ The list of 25 high-frequency words

▶ 25 High-Frequency Words Assessment—Individual Record form

▶ 25 High-Frequency Words Assessment—Class Record form

Why Use It   The assessments are designed to give you a range of assessment options depending on student ability. Each of the high-frequency assessments includes a greater number of words that gradually increase in difficulty level. You may choose to begin with 25 words and move up through each one, or you can pick the list you think would be most appropriate for your students.

This assessment will give you information about children's general knowledge of easy high-frequency words as well as the particular words they know. The substitutions they make will also reveal something about their knowledge of letter/sound relationships and spelling patterns.

How to Use It
▶ Administer this assessment individually.

▶ Ask the child to read down the columns of 25 high-frequency words.

▶ On the Individual Record form, mark the child's correct responses as well as substitutions.

▶ Record the results of the assessment on the child's Individual Record.

What to Notice
▶ Words the child can read correctly

▶ Words the child can read almost correctly

▶ Letter/sound relationships the child controls

Read the words:

no	so	go
is	on	it
can	in	do
me	up	an
you	am	the
and	we	my
he	like	to
at	see	
a	I	

25 High-Frequency Words Assessment—**Individual Record**

Name _____ Grade _____ Date _____

Directions: Use the high-frequency word list. Slide a card under each word and ask the child to read it. Check (✓) accurate responses and note substitutions. Calculate number of known words. Evaluate substitutions to determine features to which children are attending.

Word	✓	Substitution
no		
is		
can		
me		
you		
and		
he		
at		
a		
so		
on		
in		
up		
am		
we		
like		
see		
I		
go		
it		
do		
an		
the		
my		
to		
Total		

25 High-Frequency Words Assessment—**Class Record**

Names of Children

no													
is													
can													
me													
you													
and													
he													
at													
a													
so													
on													
in													
up													
am													
we													
like													
see													
I													
go													
it													
do													
an													
the													
my													
to													
Total													

Reading High-Frequency Words: **50 Words**

Description   Children read lists of high-frequency words.

You Need
▶ High-Frequency Word List

▶ 50 High-Frequency Words Assessment—Individual Record

▶ 50 High-Frequency Words Assessment—Class Record

Why Use It   The assessments are designed to give you a range of assessment options depending on student ability. Each of the high-frequency assessments includes a greater number of words that gradually increase in difficulty level. You may choose to begin with 25 words and move up through each one, or you can pick the list you think would be most appropriate for your students.

This assessment will give you information about children's knowledge of high-frequency words as well as the particular words they know. If many children miss the same words, it will help you decide which high-frequency words to include in lessons and to attend to in reading and writing.

▶ Administer this assessment individually to achieve an inventory of the high-frequency words each child knows and the words that will be productive to focus on in teaching. You can administer the assessment in one sitting or have the student do a column of words at a time.

▶ Ask the child to read each word. Record the child's correct responses with a check in the column, and record substitutions if the child misreads the word. If the child makes no response, say, "Try it." If the child still does not respond, leave the box blank. (If a child has difficulty with one out of three words, stop the assessment.)

What to Notice
▶ Number of high-frequency words read accurately

▶ Specific known words

▶ Words almost known

Phonics & Word Analysis

Read the words:

all	girl	not	she
are	got	now	sit
as	had	of	then
ball	has	or	they
be	her	out	this
boy	him	play	too
by	his	put	us
come	how	ran	was
day	if	read	went
did	jump	run	will
eat	look	sat	yes
for	man	saw	
get	mom	say	

50 High-Frequency Words Assessment—**Individual Record**

Name _____ Grade _____ Date _____

Directions: Use the high-frequency word list. Slide a card under each word and ask the child to read it. Check (✓) accurate responses and note substitutions. Calculate number of known words. Evaluate substitutions to determine features to which children are attending.

Word	✓	Substitution
all		
are		
as		
ball		
be		
boy		
by		
come		
day		
did		
eat		
for		
get		
girl		
got		
had		
has		
her		
him		
his		
how		
if		
jump		
look		
man		
Subtotal		

Word	✓	Substitution
mom		
not		
now		
of		
or		
out		
play		
put		
ran		
read		
run		
sat		
saw		
say		
she		
sit		
then		
they		
this		
too		
us		
was		
went		
will		
yes		
Subtotal		

Total number of known words: _____

© 2011, 2008 by Irene C. Fountas and Gay Su Pinnell. Portsmouth, NH: Heinemann. This page may be photocopied.

Phonics & Word Analysis

50 High-Frequency Words Assessment—**Class Record**

Name	Total number of known words
1.	
2.	
3.	
4.	
5.	
6.	
7.	
8.	
9.	
10.	
11.	
12.	
13.	
14.	
15.	
16.	
17.	
18.	
19.	
20.	
21.	
22.	
23.	
24.	
25.	
26.	
27.	
28.	

Notes

Reading High-Frequency Words: **100 Words**

Description   Children read a list of high-frequency words.

You Need
- 100 High-Frequency Words, Lists 1, 2, 3, 4, and 5
- 100 High-Frequency Words Assessment—Individual Record form
- 100 High-Frequency Words Assessment—Class Record form

Why Use It   The assessments are designed to give you a range of assessment options depending on student ability. Each of the high-frequency assessments includes a greater number of words that gradually increase in difficulty level. You may choose to begin with 25 words and move up through each one, or you can pick the list you think would be most appropriate for your students.

This assessment will tell you the extent of the children's knowledge of high-frequency words as well as the particular words they know. Their substitutions will tell you what word parts they notice.

Children need to be able to read a large number of high-frequency words. However, don't build your phonics and word-solving program around memorizing words; using patterns and parts (for example, using phonograms, letter clusters, and affixes) are more powerful strategies.

How to Use It
- Administer this test individually.
- Begin with the 45 easier high-frequency words included on Lists 1, 2, and 3. Work with one list at a time. If you think they are very easy, use the 55 additional high-frequency words on Lists 4 and 5. If these words are still too easy for your children, move to the next assessment.
- Ask the child to read the list of words you've selected.
- Children should be able to read the list quickly. Don't spend too much time on any word; tell the child to skip it and go on. If children are missing or refusing to attempt a large number of words, suggest they look down the list to see if there are any they know or stop the assessment.
- Record the child's correct responses as well as substitutions on the Individual Record form

What to Notice
- Number of high-frequency words read accurately
- Speed of word recognition
- Partially correct attempts or parts of words known
- Degree of difficulty of known words

100 High-Frequency Words, **page 1**

Read the words:

List 1	List 2	List 3
than	have	over
about	there	ride
back	any	don't
after	into	said
I'm	just	that
been	little	one
big	make	with
came	before	five
away	two	their
your	four	what
who	mother	but
when	where	here
them	very	going
because	could	our
from	were	three

Phonics & Word Analysis

100 High-Frequency Words, **page 2**

Read the words:

List 4		List 5	
want	take	books	sleep
able	dad	good	love
bad	hide	help	much
give	almost	city	stay
today	dog	write	name
week	anything	top	new
something	home	room	paper
bus	down	under	rain
year	become	fast	door
can't	end	hill	fun
tell	behind	know	sky
across	fish	use	both
world	why	let	time
cat	car	place	

Phonics & Word Analysis

100 High-Frequency Words Assessment—**Individual Record**

Name _____ Grade _____ Date _____

Directions: Use the most appropriate high-frequency word list. Ask the child to read each word. Check (✓) accurate responses and note substitutions. Calculate number of known words. Evaluate substitutions to determine features to which children are attending.

List 1	✓or write substitution	List 2	✓or write substitution	List 3	✓or write substitution
than		have		over	
about		there		ride	
back		any		don't	
after		into		said	
I'm		just		that	
been		little		one	
big		make		with	
came		before		five	
away		two		their	
your		four		what	
who		mother		but	
when		where		here	
them		very		going	
because		could		our	
from		were		three	
Subtotal		**Subtotal**		**Subtotal**	

Total number of known words: _____

100 High-Frequency Words Assessment—**Individual Record** *continued*

List 4	✓or write substitution
want	
able	
bad	
give	
today	
week	
something	
bus	
year	
can't	
tell	
across	
world	
cat	
take	
dad	
hide	
almost	
dog	
anything	
home	
down	
become	
end	
behind	
fish	
why	
car	
Subtotal	

List 5	✓or write substitution
books	
good	
help	
city	
write	
top	
room	
under	
fast	
hill	
know	
use	
let	
place	
sleep	
love	
much	
stay	
name	
new	
paper	
rain	
door	
fun	
sky	
both	
time	
Subtotal	

Total number of known words: _____

Phonics & Word Analysis

100 High-Frequency Words Assessment—**Class Record**

Name	Total number of known words
1.	
2.	
3.	
4.	
5.	
6.	
7.	
8.	
9.	
10.	
11.	
12.	
13.	
14.	
15.	
16.	
17.	
18.	
19.	
20.	
21.	
22.	
23.	
24.	
25.	
26.	
27.	
28.	

Notes

Reading High-Frequency Words: **200 Words**

Description Children read a list of high-frequency words.

You Need
- ▶ 200 High-Frequency Words, Lists 1, 2, 3, 4, and 5
- ▶ 200 High-Frequency Words Assessment—Individual Record form
- ▶ 200 High-Frequency Words Assessment—Class Record form

Why Use It The assessments are designed to give you a range of assessment options depending on student ability. Each of the high-frequency assessments includes a greater number of words that gradually increase in difficulty level. You may choose to begin with 25 words and move up through each one, or you can pick the list you think would be most appropriate for your students.

This assessment will tell you the extent of the children's knowledge of high-frequency words as well as the particular words they know. Their substitutions will tell you what word parts they notice.

Children need to be able to read a large number of high-frequency words. However, don't build your phonics and word-solving program around memorizing words; using patterns and parts (for example, using phonograms, letter clusters, and affixes) are more powerful strategies.

How to Use It
- ▶ Administer this test individually.
- ▶ Begin with the 80 easier high-frequency words included on Lists 1, 2, and 3. Work with one list at a time. If you think they are very easy, use the 120 additional high-frequency words on Lists 4 and 5.
- ▶ Ask the child to read the list of words you've selected.
- ▶ Children should be able to read the list quickly. Don't spend too much time on any word; tell the child to skip it and go on. If children are missing or refusing to attempt a large number of words, suggest they look down the list to see if there are any they know or stop the assessment.
- ▶ Record the child's correct responses as well as substitutions on the Individual Record form.

What to Notice
- ▶ Number of high-frequency words read accurately
- ▶ Speed of word recognition
- ▶ Partially correct attempts or parts of words known
- ▶ Degree of difficulty of known words

200 High-Frequency Words, **page 1**

Read the words:

List 1	List 2	List 3
sea	happy	house
wrote	catch	start
again	third	grew
carry	night	way
wait	goes	friend
each	last	story
feel	school	street
always	walk	above
first	ten	find
ask	change	between
food	outside	every
work	part	should
brother	live	father
through	party	watch
funny	game	children
gave	try	hid
things	pick	enough
close	right	dark
even	teach	great
grow	until	inside
gone	second	light
same	deep	seen
knew	view	during
begin	grade	worn
winter	snow	wrong
must	does	you're
stop	together	

200 High-Frequency Words, **page 2**

Read the words:

List 4		List 5	
several	river	follow	being
never	might	pretty	also
getting	air	couldn't	slowly
earth	I'd	happen	bring
group	suddenly	themselves	hear
baby	easy	direction	often
everything	finally	nothing	page
high	everyone	life	store
wouldn't	hold	someone	while
probably	special	without	however
through	animal	instead	kids
against	lost	either	check
hour	beautiful	lunch	listen
fight	need	important	few
once	job	less	stuff
best	sick	own	problem
ready	maybe	think	such
free	land	round	cleans
show	next	scared	teacher
build	old	person	dream
draw	window	short	sister
state	better	add	plan
kind	written	wanted	they're
circle	favorite	young	possible
large	care	question	thought
doing	myself	yourself	really
family	since	answer	understand
clothes	picture	money	near
hand	class	simple	rest
different	idea	more	soon

Phonics & Word Analysis

200 High-Frequency Words Assessment—**Individual Record, page 1**

Name _____ Grade _____ Date _____

Directions: Use the most appropriate high-frequency word list. Ask the child to read each word. Check (✓) accurate responses and note substitutions. Calculate number of known words. Evaluate substitutions to determine features to which children are attending.

List 1	✓ or write substitution		List 2	✓ or write substitution		List 3	✓ or write substitution
sea			happy			house	
wrote			catch			start	
again			third			grew	
carry			night			way	
wait			goes			friend	
each			last			story	
feel			school			street	
always			walk			above	
first			ten			find	
ask			change			between	
food			outside			every	
work			part			should	
brother			live			father	
through			party			watch	
funny			game			children	
gave			try			hid	
things			pick			enough	
close			right			dark	
even			teach			great	
grow			until			inside	
gone			second			light	
same			deep			seen	
knew			view			during	
begin			grade			worn	
winter			snow			wrong	
must			does			you're	
stop			together				
Subtotal			**Subtotal**			**Subtotal**	

Total number of known words: _____

200 High-Frequency Words Assessment—**Individual Record, page 2**

List 4	✓ or write substitution
several	
never	
getting	
earth	
group	
baby	
everything	
high	
wouldn't	
probably	
through	
against	
hour	
fight	
once	
best	
ready	
free	
show	
build	
draw	
state	
kind	
circle	
large	
doing	
family	
clothes	
hand	
different	
Subtotal	

List 4	✓ or write substitution
river	
might	
air	
I'd	
suddenly	
easy	
finally	
everyone	
hold	
special	
animal	
lost	
beautiful	
need	
job	
sick	
maybe	
land	
next	
old	
window	
better	
written	
favorite	
care	
myself	
since	
picture	
class	
idea	
Subtotal	

Total number of known words: _____

Phonics & Word Analysis

200 High-Frequency Words Assessment—**Individual Record, page 3**

List 5	✓ or write substitution	List 5	✓ or write substitution
follow		being	
pretty		also	
couldn't		slowly	
happen		bring	
themselves		hear	
direction		often	
nothing		page	
life		store	
someone		while	
without		however	
instead		kids	
either		check	
lunch		listen	
important		few	
less		stuff	
own		problem	
think		such	
round		cleans	
scared		teacher	
person		dream	
short		sister	
add		plan	
wanted		they're	
young		possible	
question		thought	
yourself		really	
answer		understand	
money		near	
simple		rest	
more		soon	
Subtotal		**Subtotal**	

Total number of known words: _____

200 High-Frequency Words Assessment—**Class Record**

Name	Total number of known words
1.	
2.	
3.	
4.	
5.	
6.	
7.	
8.	
9.	
10.	
11.	
12.	
13.	
14.	
15.	
16.	
17.	
18.	
19.	
20.	
21.	
22.	
23.	
24.	
25.	
26.	
27.	
28.	

Notes

Phonics & Word Analysis

Phonological Awareness: **Initial Sounds**

Description   Children identify pictures with the same initial sound as a spoken word.

Children are given four picture cards and told the name of each picture. They say the sound and point to or say the picture that begins with the same sound. The child is also asked to produce orally the beginning sound for an orally presented word that matches one of the given pictures.

You Need
▷ Initial Sounds Picture Cards—Sheets 1 and 2
▷ Phonological Awareness Assessment—Individual Record form
▷ Phonological Awareness Assessment—Class Record form

Why Use It   This assessment will tell you whether children can hear and match initial sounds in words.

How to Use It
▷ Administer this test individually.
▷ Begin by showing the child four picture cards: *bear, hat, dog,* and *milk*. Say the name of each picture. Then hold up the picture card for *bird*, say the name, and ask the child to find the other picture card that starts with the same sound. Repeat using *horse, desk,* and *mouse*.
▷ Then, say the name of four of the pictures: *bird, horse, desk,* and *mouse* and ask the child to orally produce the initial sound.
▷ Record the child's correct responses as well as substitutions on the Individual Record form.
▷ Show the child four more picture cards: *cat, fan, ladder,* and *pencil*. Say the name of each picture. Use *cake, fire, lion,* and *penguin* and ask the child to find the other picture card that starts with the same sound.
▷ Then, say the names: *cake, fire, lion,* and *penguin*. Ask the child to orally produce the initial sound.
▷ Record the child's correct responses as well as substitutions on the Individual Record form.

What to Notice
▷ Number of sounds the child can correctly match
▷ Whether children can orally produce the initial sound of a word they have heard

Initial Sounds Picture Cards—**Sheet 1**

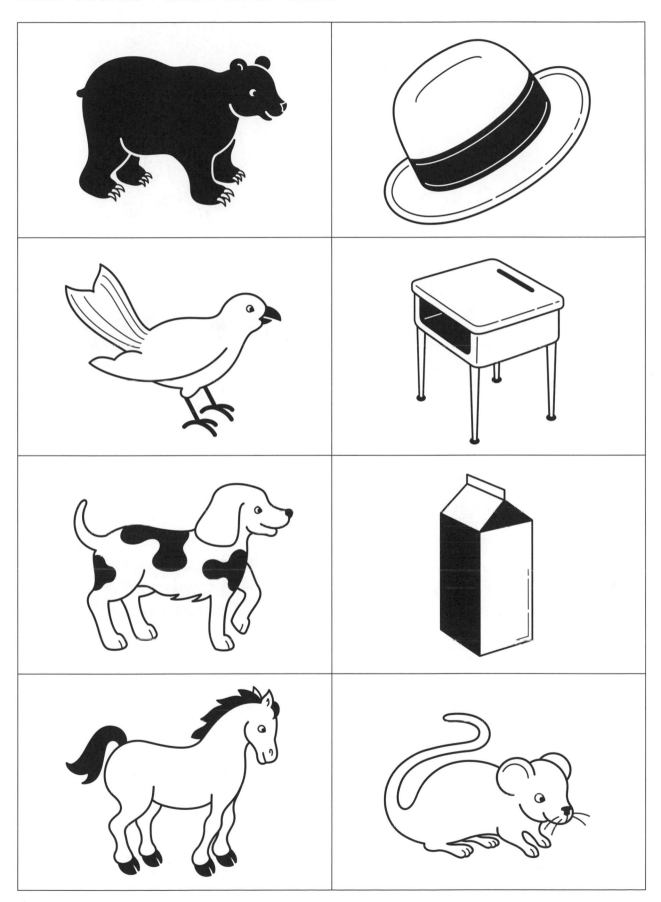

© 2011, 2008 by Irene C. Fountas and Gay Su Pinnell. Portsmouth, NH: Heinemann. This page may be photocopied.

Phonics & Word Analysis

Initial Sounds Picture Cards—**Sheet 2**

Phonological Awareness: **Blending Words**

Description   Children hear and say the individual sounds in a word and then blend the sounds to say the word.

You Need
▶ Phonological Awareness Assessment—Individual Record form
▶ Phonological Awareness Assessment—Class Record form

Why Use It   This assessment will help you learn whether children can take individual sounds and blend them together. This ability helps children take words apart to solve them. Some children will grasp this principle with only a few demonstrations. Use this assessment to determine how much experience children need in blending sounds.

How to Use It
▶ Administer this task individually so you can closely observe behavior. Tell the child you are going to say the sounds of a word: "I will say the sounds of a word. Then you say the whole word smoothly." Use /m/-/ă/-/t/, *mat*, as an example. Continue with:

/h/-/ĭ/-/d/ [hid]

/w/-/ĭ/-/sh/ [wish]

/p/-/ŏ/-/t/ [pot]

/f/-/ē/-/t/ [feet]

/l/-/o͝o/-/k/ [look]

/t/-/ā/-/k/ [take]

/m/-/o͞o/-/n/ [moon]

/n/-/ŭ/-/t/ [nut]

/r/-/ă/-/p/ [rap]

/ch/-/ĭ/-/l/ [chill]

▶ Record results on the child's Individual Record. Consider the task mastered if a child can blend eight of the ten words.

What to Notice
▶ Ability to listen to and understand the task
▶ Ability to blend the sounds

© 2011, 2008 by Irene C. Fountas and Gay Su Pinnell. Portsmouth, NH: Heinemann. This page may be photocopied.

Phonics & Word Analysis

Phonological Awareness: **Segmenting Words**

Description Children say a word and then say the individual sounds separately but in sequence.

You Need
- ▶ Phonological Awareness Assessment—Individual Record form
- ▶ Phonological Awareness Assessment—Class Record form

Why Use It This assessment will help you learn whether children can take a word and segment it into individual sounds. This ability helps children in both spelling and decoding. Some children may understand this principle with only a few demonstrations. Others will need more experience.

How to Use It
- ▶ Administer this assessment individually so you can closely observe behavior. Say the word and ask the child to say the segmented sounds in the word: "I am going to say a word. Then you say the sounds in the word, like this: *fan*, /f/-/ă/-/n/." Then continue with:

  wet [/w/-/ĕ/-/t/]

  vase [/v/-/ā/-/s/]

  trip [/t/-/r/-/ĭ/-/p/]

  miss [/m/-/ĭ/-/s/]

  duck [/d/-/ŭ/-/k/]

  pad [/p/-/ă/-/d/]

  fast /f/-/ă/-/s/-/t/]

  kick [/k/-/ĭ/-/k/]

  tool [/t/-/o͞o/-/l/]

  boat [/b/-/ō/-/t/]

- ▶ Record results on the child's Individual Record. Consider the task mastered if a child can segment eight of the ten words.

What to Notice
- ▶ Ability to listen to and understand the task
- ▶ Ability to say each sound
- ▶ Ability to say sounds in sequence

Phonological Awareness: **Rhyming**

Description Children match words that sound alike in the ending part (rime).

You Need
▶ Rhyming Cards—Sheets 1 and 2

▶ Phonological Awareness Assessment—Individual Record form

▶ Phonological Awareness Assessment—Class Record form

Why Use It This assessment will help you learn the degree to which children can hear and make connections between words that rhyme. Recognizing rhymes is foundational to recognizing word parts and beginning to analyze words.

How to Use It
▶ Have children match picture cards representing pairs of words that rhyme, saying the words to check them. Start by demonstrating with one or two easy examples to help children understand the task. Sample words are *bee, tree; fish, dish; fan, van; box, socks; star, car*.

▶ Administering the assessment individually will not take much time and will give you important insight into the child's processing. For example, a child who connects *fish* and *fan* is making a good sound analysis that does not meet the requirements of the task. You can intervene with a few examples of rhymes (noting your support on the record sheet) to see whether he now grasps the idea or continues to be confused.

▶ Record each child's responses on the Individual Record form. There is enough space for a longer test, but you do not need many items to get an idea of whether the child understands the concept.

What to Notice
▶ Ability to identify and say labels of objects represented in pictures

▶ Ability to listen for and identify sound patterns (rhymes) in words

▶ Ability to connect a sound pattern with another sound pattern that is similar

▶ Speed with which the child identifies similar sound patterns (rhymes)

Phonics & Word Analysis

Rhyming Cards—**Sheet 1**

Name _____

Match the rhymes.

Rhyming Cards—**Sheet 2**

Name _____

Match the rhymes.

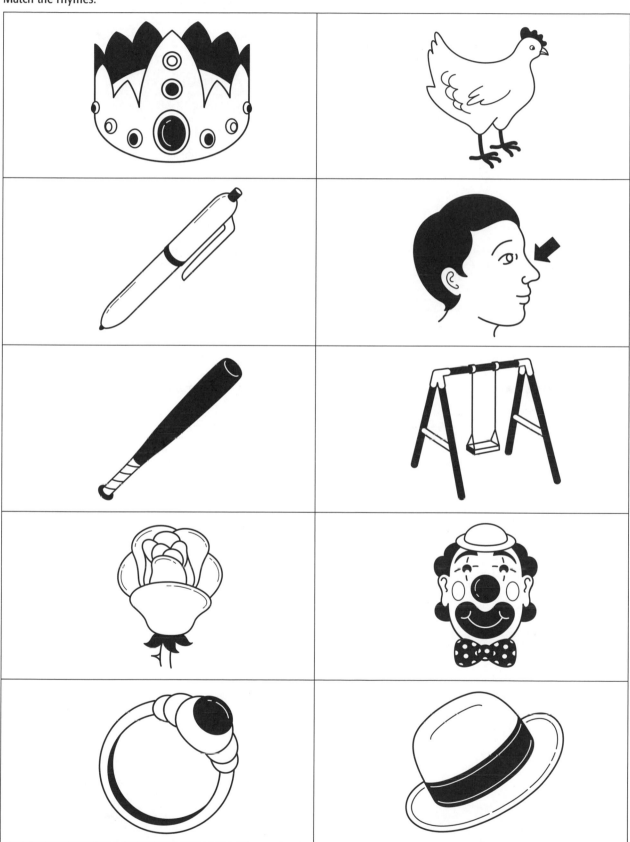

Phonics & Word Analysis

Phonological Awareness Assessment—**Individual Record**

Name _____   Grade _____   Date _____

Initial Sounds Assessment

	Matching (✓ or substitutions)	Oral (✓ or substitutions)
b /b/		
h /h/		
d /d/		
m /m/		
c /k/		
f /f/		
l /l/		
p /p/		
Total		

Blending Assessment

	Scoring (✓)
/h/-/ĭ/-/d/ [hid]	
/w/-/ĭ/-/sh/ [wish]	
/p/-/ŏ/-/t/ [pot]	
/f/-/ē/-/t/ [feet]	
/l/-/oo/-/k/ [look]	
/t/-/ā/-/k/ [take]	
/m/-/o͞o/-/n/ [moon]	
/n/-/ŭ/-/t/ [nut]	
/r/-/ă/-/p/ [rap]	
/ch/-/ĭ/-/l/ [chill]	
Total	

Segmenting Assessment

	Scoring (✓)
wet [/w/-/ĕ/-/t/]	
vase [/v/-/ā/-/s/]	
trip [/t/-/r/-/ĭ/-/p/]	
miss [/m/-/ĭ/-/s/]	
duck [/d/-/ŭ/-/k/]	
pad [/p/-/ă/-/d/]	
fast [/f/-/ă/-/s/-/t/]	
kick [/k/-/ĭ/-/k/]	
tool [/t/-/o͞o/-/l/]	
boat [/b/-/ō/-/t/]	
Total	

Rhyming Assessment

	Scoring (✓)
bee/tree	
fish/dish	
fan/van	
box/socks	
star/car	
rose/nose	
pen/hen	
bat/hat	
crown/clown	
ring/swing	
Total	

Phonological Awareness Assessment—**Class Record**

Name	Initial Sounds Assessment	Blending Assessment	Segmenting Assessment	Rhyming Assessment
1.				
2.				
3.				
4.				
5.				
6.				
7.				
8.				
9.				
10.				
11.				
12.				
13.				
14.				
15.				
16.				
17.				
18.				
19.				
20.				
21.				
22.				
23.				
24.				
25.				
26.				
27.				

Notes

Phonics & Word Analysis

Word Writing

Description   Children write all of the words they can write within a designated time limit.

You Need
▷ Blank paper with a space for children to write their name.

▷ Word Writing—Class Record form

Why Use It   This assessment will give you a rich inventory of what children control in terms of writing. Examining this document will not only tell you the words that children can spell accurately but also what they are thinking about words and how they work. You can note attempts as well as evidence that children are placing words into categories. You can think about how their strengths in writing words can support reading.

How to Use It
▷ Early in the year, you may want to administer this assessment individually so that you can prompt children with familiar words, for example *I, the, it, is, in* (refer to the high-frequency word lists on pages 179–199).

▷ At your signal, children write their names and then write all the words they know until you say stop. (Give them between five and ten minutes.) Encourage children to try words even if they think they don't know how to spell them with all the letters.

▷ Suggested language: "We are going to do something special today. Each of you is going to write as many words as you can. Are you thinking of a word you know you can write?" Get some suggestions from the children. "Start by writing your name on the line at the top of the page." Give children time to write their name. "Write words carefully. If you are not sure how to write a word, just try it. Try to leave spaces between your words so that I can read them."

▷ Early in the year, make this assessment informal. You do not need to hide the print on the walls. In fact, it will be interesting to note how children are using the resources in the classroom. Midyear or later, you may want to make assessment more challenging by being sure that children perform the task without access to print on the walls.

▷ Analyze the child's writing to notice what letter/sound relationships and spelling patterns the child controls.

What to Notice
▷ Awareness of his own inventory of words
- Knowledge of the way one word leads to another, revealing connections between words as well as categories
- Use of phonograms and spelling patterns
- Ease and fluency in constructing words
- Use of endings to make several words from a root word
- Ability to hear the sounds in words
- Ability to represent sounds with letters
- Knowledge of high-frequency word patterns
- Ability to use and connect word parts

Word Writing

An example of one child's writing is included below. Michael has a score of 59 accurately written words. In addition, notice that he:

▶ has many different ways of getting to words.

▶ began with his name and then wrote another name he knew.

▶ wrote simple, high-frequency words in the first column but seemed to connect them because of similar patterns (*in, is, it; there, here*).

▶ added *s* to *book*, making another word, as well as adding *ing* and *ed* to *play*.

▶ wrote *good* and then thought of *go*, perhaps noting their similarity visually.

▶ wrote *you* and then *your*.

▶ wrote *into* and then wrote two other forms of the word *to*, which he wrote instantly because he knew them.

▶ constructed some words without having to think about sounds and letters.

▶ added *d* to *see* to produce *seed*.

▶ made one attempt that resulted in inaccurate spelling—*ttat* for *that*, which may have been the result of hurrying or not noticing (he knows how to use *th* because he spelled *that* correctly later in the sequence, after *them, they,* and *then*).

Word Writing—**Class Record**

Name	Total words	Notes
1.		
2.		
3.		
4.		
5.		
6.		
7.		
8.		
9.		
10.		
11.		
12.		
13.		
14.		
15.		
16.		
17.		
18.		
19.		
20.		
21.		
22.		
23.		
24.		
25.		
26.		
27.		
28.		

Writing Picture Names

Description Children say words slowly and write the sounds they hear.

You Need
▶ Writing Picture Names—Sheets 1 and 2
▶ Writing Picture Names Assessment—Class Record form

Why Use It This assessment will give you information about whether children can say words slowly, think about the sounds in the words, and record some of them by remembering and writing associated letters. These are complex sets of information. Children are being asked to say and hear a sound, associate it with a letter and the directional movements needed to write the letter, and then use these movements to write the letter in a legible form.

How to Use It
▶ Ask children to attempt to write the letters in a series of words that you say as you hold up a picture card that represents the word. Suggested words:

   1. *cat* (three phonemes), *mug* (three phonemes), *nine* (three phonemes), *bed* (three phonemes), *lock* (three phonemes), *desk* (four phonemes), *pin* (three phonemes), and *doll* (three phonemes).

   2. *truck* (four phonemes), *feet* (three phonemes), *bag* (three phonemes), *five* (three phonemes), *nose* (three phonemes), *gum* (three phonemes), *map* (three phonemes), and *seal* (three phonemes).

▶ Record the number of different phonemes that each child can represent, for a maximum score of 25 on each list, on the Class Record.

What to Notice
▶ Ability to identify labels for objects represented by pictures
▶ Ability to say words very slowly, to hear each of the sounds
▶ Ability to say, hear, and identify the individual sounds in words
▶ Ability to form letters
▶ The sequence of sounds the child hears and records

Writing Picture Names, sheet 1

_____

_____   _____

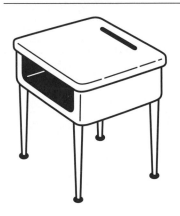

_____   _____

_____   _____

Phonics & Word Analysis

Writing Picture Names, sheet 2

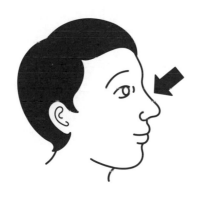

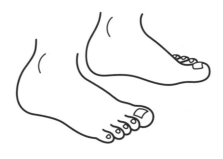

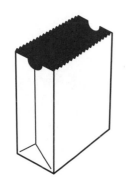

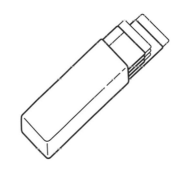

Writing Picture Names Assessment—**Class Record**

Date _____

Name	Writing Words List 1 (max = 25)	Writing Words List 2 (max = 25)
1.		
2.		
3.		
4.		
5.		
6.		
7.		
8.		
9.		
10.		
11.		
12.		
13.		
14.		
15.		
16.		
17.		
18.		
19.		
20.		
21.		
22.		
23.		
24.		
25.		
26.		
27.		
28.		

Phonograms

Description   Children read words with simple phonogram patterns.

You Need
▶ Phonogram Word Lists

▶ Phonograms Assessment—Individual Record form

▶ Phonograms Assessment—Class Record form

Why Use It   Regular phonogram patterns are very helpful to beginning readers because knowing these patterns helps them decode many new words. Also, they will decode words more efficiently when they are able to deal with larger chunks of letters. Use this assessment to learn which phonograms most of your children can already read, those they can almost read, and those they need to learn. Children who can read most of the words on these lists probably do not need to work on phonograms, although they may find it helpful to summarize their learning and sort words. You can also identify children who do not understand the concept of word patterns or have very little knowledge.

How to Use It
▶ Administer this test individually (use one of the included lists or prepare one of your own).

▶ If you are working with children near the beginning of first grade, you may want to begin with List 1, which includes very simple phonograms. If children are more advanced and you think that List 1 will be too easy, begin with List 2, which has the same phonograms with consonant clusters at the beginning.

▶ Check a child's reading of between ten and fifteen words at a time over several days. Note accurate responses with a ✓ and note substitutions, spelling nonword attempts phonetically.

▶ Use the Individual Record form to keep an ongoing record of each child's ability to read words with these regular phonogram patterns.

What to Notice
▶ Number of spelling patterns the child can recognize accurately

▶ Speed in recognizing patterns

Phonogram Word Lists

List 1	List 2	List 3	List 4
not	shot	ate	chore
man	slam	mane	pile
sit	twig	flake	dive
hen	when	bite	made
pan	drop	sing	smell
day	flap	flame	race
fat	slit	rag	stale
dog	sled	plane	cage
nap	bran	same	stage
tap	ship	drape	sale
pig	shut	plate	space
net	chin	drag	hive
tip	wet	bike	shade
red	plan	white	robe
nut	frog	strike	while
pin	spray	slime	poke
sad	that	tape	spell
rug	plug	bring	bore
hop	glad	rake	choke
jam	flip	dine	bell

Phonograms Assessment—**Individual Record**

Name _____ Grade _____

Directions: Ask the child to read each word. Check (✓) accurate responses and note substitutions. Calculate the score for each list.

List 1

Date _____

Word	✓
not	
man	
sit	
hen	
pan	
day	
fat	
dog	
nap	
tap	
pig	
net	
tip	
red	
nut	
pin	
sad	
rug	
hop	
jam	
Score	/20

List 2

Date _____

Word	✓
shot	
slam	
twig	
when	
drop	
flap	
slit	
sled	
bran	
ship	
shut	
chin	
wet	
plan	
frog	
spray	
that	
plug	
glad	
flip	
Score	/20

List 3

Date _____

Word	✓
ate	
mane	
flake	
bite	
sing	
flame	
rag	
plane	
same	
drape	
plate	
drag	
bike	
white	
strike	
slime	
tape	
bring	
rake	
dine	
Score	/20

List 4

Date _____

Word	✓
chore	
pile	
dive	
made	
smell	
race	
stale	
cage	
stage	
sale	
space	
hive	
shade	
robe	
while	
poke	
spell	
bore	
choke	
bell	
Score	/20

Phonograms Assessment—**Class Record**

Name	Total score
1.	
2.	
3.	
4.	
5.	
6.	
7.	
8.	
9.	
10.	
11.	
12.	
13.	
14.	
15.	
16.	
17.	
18.	
19.	
20.	
21.	
22.	
23.	
24.	
25.	
26.	
27.	
28.	

Notes

Consonant Blends

Description   Children read words, marking the consonant blends, or words with two or three consonant sounds together.

You Need
- ▷ Consonant Blends Word List
- ▷ Consonant Blends Assessment—Class Record form

Why Use It   This assessment will provide information about the children's ability to recognize consonant blends within words and use that information to read words.

How to Use It
- ▷ Administer this assessment individually using the Consonant Blends Word List.
- ▷ Ask the child to read the list of words, going down each column.
- ▷ Score for accuracy and note substitutions.
- ▷ Use the Word List as the child's Individual Record form. Record the results on the Class Record form.
- ▷ For additional information, give the child a copy of the words, and ask him to highlight or circle all of the consonant blends he can find. Observe the speed and confidence he shows in finding consonant blends, as well as the accuracy. You can administer this task as a timed group assessment.

What to Notice
- ▷ Ability to use knowledge of consonant blends to read words
- ▷ Number of words with consonant blends the child can read
- ▷ Specific consonant blends the child controls in reading

Phonics & Word Analysis

Consonant Blends Word List

Name _____   Date _____

Read the words and circle or highlight the consonant clusters in each one.

spread	driving
dusk	float
train	creek
smooth	please
stream	frame
clever	splice
best	strike

Consonant Blends Assessment—**Class Record**

Two-Letter Blends

Three-Letter Blends

Name	dusk	train	smooth	clever	float	creek	please	best	driving	frame	spread	stream	splice	strike
1.														
2.														
3.														
4.														
5.														
6.														
7.														
8.														
9.														
10.														
11.														
12.														
13.														
14.														
15.														
16.														
17.														
18.														
19.														
20.														

Phonics & Word Analysis

Vowel Clusters

Description Children read words with vowels that appear together and represent one sound.

You Need
▷ Vowel Clusters, Word Lists 1, 2, and 3

▷ Vowel Clusters Assessment—Individual Record form

▷ Vowel Clusters Assessment—Class Record form

Why Use It Children need to learn the various vowel combinations that often appear together in words. This knowledge will help them build the capacity to remember how words "look" rather than relying only on the sound. Knowing several examples for each vowel cluster will help children read new words.

How to Use It
▷ Begin by reviewing the list of words found on the Individual Record. Select the list that is most appropriate for your group of children. List 1 contains simple vowel combinations (*ee, ea, ai, oa*) that children may have learned in second grade. For an experienced group, you may want to begin with List 2, going on to List 3 if children find the tasks very easy.

▷ Have children read the list individually. Record their responses on the Individual Record by checking words read accurately and recording substitutions.

▷ It is not necessary for the child to produce 100% accuracy of all vowel combinations; consider the principle learned if there is a high level of accuracy. You will not need to provide a lesson on every vowel combination. If children know the principle and quite a few combinations, they will learn more from reading and writing.

What to Notice
▷ Number of words with vowel clusters the child can read

▷ Number of words with vowel clusters for which the child can provide accurate representation of the cluster

▷ Particular vowel clusters the child controls in reading

Vowel Clusters, **Word List 1**

seal	peel
sail	sweet
stain	heat
meal	braid
boat	lean
main	soap
real	train
rain	seen
speak	goat
sheets	neat
float	road
bean	

Vowel Clusters, **Word List 2**

claw	grief
cows	grow
crawl	house
toe	moon
spoon	snow
new	pout
few	plow
good	spray
gray	thief
book	wood

Vowel Clusters, **Word List 3**

pour	hair
pearl	tier
boar	poor
air	rear
career	floor
your	peer
pier	soar

Vowel Clusters Assessment—**Individual Record**

Name _____ Age _____ Grade _____ Date _____

List 1

Vowel Cluster	✓ if the child shows good control of vowel cluster
seal	
sail	
stain	
meal	
boat	
main	
real	
rain	
speak	
sheets	
float	
bean	
peel	
sweet	
heat	
braid	
lean	
soap	
train	
seen	
goat	
neat	
road	
Total	

ee	
ea	
ai	
oa	

List 2

Vowel Cluster	✓ if the child shows good control of vowel cluster
claw	
cows	
crawl	
toe	
spoon	
new	
few	
good	
gray	
book	
grief	
grow	
house	
moon	
snow	
pout	
plow	
spray	
thief	
wood	
Total	

ay		**oo**	
aw		**ou**	
ew		**ow**	
ie		**oe**	

List 3

Vowel Cluster	✓ if the child shows good control of vowel cluster
pour	
pearl	
boar	
air	
career	
your	
pier	
hair	
tier	
poor	
rear	
floor	
peer	
soar	
Total	

eer		**ier**	
ear		**our**	
air		**oor**	
oar			

Vowel Clusters Assessment—**Class Record**

✓ if child accurately represented
the vowel cluster at least once

Name	List 1 Easy				List 2 More Difficult Vowel Clusters										List 3 Advanced *r*-Controlled						
	ee	ea	ai	oa	ay	aw	ew	ie	oo	ou	ow	oe	eer	ear	air	oar	ier	our	oor
1.																			
2.																			
3.																			
4.																			
5.																			
6.																			
7.																			
8.																			
9.																			
10.																			
11.																			
12.																			
13.																			
14.																			
15.																			
16.																			
17.																			
18.																			
19.																			
20.																			
21.																			
22.																			
23.																			
24.																			
25.																			

Suffixes

Description	Children read words with suffixes that change the part of speech.
You Need	▶ Words with Suffixes sheet
	▶ Suffixes—Class Record form
Why Use It	This assessment will help you learn whether the children understand the concept that a suffix can change the part of speech and whether they can apply their knowledge of suffixes to read words.
How to Use It	▶ Administer the assessment individually.
	▶ Give the child a copy of the Words with Suffixes sheet. Say the base word (Column 1) for the child and then ask her to read the word with the suffix.
	▶ As an alternative, use either the base word or the word with the suffix in a sentence and ask the child to circle the word you used. Demonstrate with the first sentence.
	▶ Record the performance on the Class Record. Check the box if the student reads both words with the suffix correctly.
What to Notice	▶ Number of words with suffixes the child can read
	▶ Particular words and suffixes the child recognizes
	▶ Speed with which the child reads words with suffixes

Words with Suffixes

Name _____ Date _____

1.	run	running
2.	write	writer
3.	work	worker
4.	quick	quickly
5.	sun	sunny
6.	like	likely
7.	high	highest
8.	build	building
9.	shine	shiny
10.	bright	brightest

Suffixes—**Class Record**

Name	-ing	-er	-ly	-y	-est
1.					
2.					
3.					
4.					
5					
6.					
7.					
8.					
9					
10.					
11.					
12.					
13.					
14					
15.					
16.					
17.					
18.					
19.					
20.					
21.					
22.					
23.					
24.					
25.					
26.					
27.					
28.					

Compound Words

Description   Children read simple compound words and identify the two words that have been put together.

You Need
▶ Compound Words list

▶ Lined paper

▶ Markers and pencils

▶ Compound Words Assessment—Individual Record form

▶ Compound Words Assessment—Class Record form

Why Use It   This assessment will help you learn whether children can read simple compound words and identify the component parts.

How to Use It
▶ Administer this assessment individually.

▶ Have the child read the 38 words on the Compound Words list. If the child finds a word difficult, prompt her once to look for a part she knows. On another copy of the form, note accurate responses and errors and score the number read correctly. Then ask the child to make a slash between the two component words.

What to Notice
▶ Number of compound words the child recognizes

▶ Specific compound words the child recognizes

▶ Specific compound words the child can take apart

Compound Words

Name _____ Date _____

airplane	grandmother
airport	haircut
anybody	headset
anything	himself
background	into
basketball	itself
bedroom	maybe
birdhouse	myself
birthday	nobody
cannot	playground
chalkboard	skateboard
cookbook	snowball
crosswalk	somebody
daytime	something
doorbell	sunshine
downstairs	today
earring	upset
everything	without
football	yourself

Compound Words Assessment—**Individual Record**

Name _____ Date _____

Compound Words			
airplane		grandmother	
airport		haircut	
anybody		headset	
anything		himself	
background		into	
basketball		itself	
bedroom		maybe	
birdhouse		myself	
birthday		nobody	
cannot		playground	
chalkboard		skateboard	
cookbook		snowball	
crosswalk		somebody	
daytime		something	
doorbell		sunshine	
downstairs		today	
earring		upset	
everything		without	
football		yourself	
	/19		/19

Compound Words Assessment—**Class Record**

Name	Number of accurate responses
1.	
2.	
3.	
4.	
5.	
6.	
7.	
8.	
9.	
10.	
11.	
12.	
13.	
14.	
15.	
16.	
17.	
18.	
19.	
20.	
21.	
22.	
23.	
24.	
25.	
26.	
27.	
28.	

One- and Two-Syllable Words

Description Children say a word, clap or tap a finger for each syllable, and then identify the number of syllables in the word.

You Need
▶ Word Cards
▶ Say and Sort Picture Cards
▶ Say and Sort Sheet
▶ One- and Two-Syllable Assessment—Individual Record form
▶ Syllable Assessments—Class Record form

Why Use It These two assessments will give evidence as to whether children hear word parts and syllable breaks. Both tasks provide information as to whether children can hear and identify syllable breaks and say the number of syllables in each word. Use this information to form small groups of children who have difficulty hearing syllables and need more work. Task #1 is a simple clapping task. You can use the words suggested here or others that you add. Task #2 requires students to say and sort words by the number of syllables in the word.

How to Use It **#1 Clap Syllables — Easy** Administer this test individually. Prepare a list of ten one- and two-syllable words, for example: *hot, absent, paper, went, pumpkin, run, monster, find, water,* and *dream*. Be sure children have heard the words before and understand them. Ask children to clap the correct number of syllables. You can check whether each child's responses are accurate for each word.

#2 Say and Sort — More Challenging Use the ten picture cards with one- and two-syllable words. Be sure children know the meaning of the words. Ask children to say each word and to sort them under the numerals (1 and 2). You can check whether each child's responses are accurate for each word. As an alternative, prepare a pencil-and-paper test in which children write the number of parts they hear next to each word.

What to Notice
▶ Number of words for which child can identify the correct number of syllables
▶ Ability to identify one- and two-syllable words
▶ Ability to represent sounds with letters
▶ Ability to represent syllables

Say and Sort Picture Cards

Say and Sort Sheet

Name _____ Date _____

Glue the picture under the right number of syllables.

1	2

One- and Two-Syllable Assessment—**Individual Record**

Name _____ Grade _____ Date _____

Directions: Ask the child to say the name of the picture on each card and sort the pictures onto the Say and Sort Sheet. Check if student identifies the syllables correctly.

Words	Identifies number of syllables correctly
pumpkin	
glass	
balloon	
apple	
dish	
dog	
cat	
mitten	
pizza	
mouse	
Notes	

Syllables in Longer Words

Description Children demonstrate that they understand the concept of syllables, can hear syllable breaks, can count the number of syllables in a word, and have a beginning understanding of where to divide a word when hyphenating.

You Need
▶ Markers and pencils
▶ Syllables in Longer Words sheet
▶ Syllable Assessments—Class Record form

Why Use It Most third-graders will be able to hear syllable breaks easily and count the number of syllables in a word. This ability to break words down into syllables is basic to word solving in both reading and writing. If you have already observed children's ability to hear syllables, you will not need to use this assessment. If some children do not seem to be breaking words down in this way, this quick assessment will help you identify those who need some small group work.

How to Use It
▶ Administer this assessment individually.

▶ Using the Syllables in Longer Words sheet, read each word aloud and have students say it softly to themselves. For each word, they place a line between syllables and circle the number of parts or syllables they hear.

▶ Use each student's sheet as an individual record. Do not be concerned about "correct" hyphenation, but notice children's use of their implicit sense of where the breaks would come in written words.

▶ If children correctly identify at least seven of the ten two-syllable words, place a ✓ by the child's name under "Identifies two syllables." Do the same for the ten three syllable and four syllable words.

What to Notice
▶ Number of words in which the child can hear and identify syllables

▶ Particular words children can read accurately

▶ Particular words that give children difficulty (for example, words with vowel pairs or consonant clusters)

▶ Ability to follow directions

▶ Speed with which children take words apart

Syllables in Longer Words

Name _____ Date _____

Say the words. Mark the syllables with a slash. Circle the number of syllables you hear in each word.

1.	absent	1 2 3 4	16.	independent	1 2 3 4
2.	differences	1 2 3 4	17.	magnificent	1 2 3 4
3.	calculator	1 2 3 4	18.	underneath	1 2 3 4
4.	flavor	1 2 3 4	19.	monster	1 2 3 4
5.	caravan	1 2 3 4	20.	tornado	1 2 3 4
6.	excuse	1 2 3 4	21.	multiply	1 2 3 4
7.	dessert	1 2 3 4	22.	water	1 2 3 4
8.	wonderful	1 2 3 4	23.	plastic	1 2 3 4
9.	different	1 2 3 4	24.	poisonous	1 2 3 4
10.	inspect	1 2 3 4	25.	pretzel	1 2 3 4
11.	habitat	1 2 3 4	26.	mysterious	1 2 3 4
12.	conversation	1 2 3 4	27.	watermelon	1 2 3 4
13.	interested	1 2 3 4	28.	demonstration	1 2 3 4
14.	vacation	1 2 3 4	29.	stubborn	1 2 3 4
15.	invention	1 2 3 4	30.	absolutely	1 2 3 4

Syllable Assessments—**Class Record**

Date _____

Name	Identifies one syllable	Identifies two syllables	Identifies three syllables	Identifies four syllables
1.				
2.				
3.				
4.				
5.				
6.				
7.				
8.				
9.				
10.				
11.				
12.				
13.				
14.				
15.				
16.				
17.				
18.				
19.				
20.				
21.				
22.				
23.				
24.				
25.				
26.				
27.				
28.				

Grade 1 Word Features Test

Description   Children read 30 words, which include a variety of features.

You Need
- Grade 1 Word Features List
- Grade 1 Word Features Test—Individual Record form
- Grade 1 Word Features Test—Class Record form

Why Use It   This assessment will give you information about which features of words children are able to attend to. The substitutions they make will also provide information about their knowledge of letter/sound relationships, spelling patterns, and word structure.

How to Use It
- Administer this assessment individually.
- Ask the child to read the list of 30 words.
- On the Individual Record form, record the child's correct responses as well as substitutions.

What to Notice
- Word features the child can read correctly
- Word features with which the child has difficulty

Grade 1 Word Features List

Read the words:

big	hole	she's
mat	ant	hammer
pet	Mom's	race
fun	puppy	jump
Kim's	seal	I'm
wave	bedroom	kiss
drop	boat	baseball
you'll	list	strip
feet	pile	bell
this	wash	white

Grade 1 Word Features Test—**Individual Record**

Name _____ Date _____

Word	✓ or substitution	Feature
big		Consonant sounds (b, g); short vowel sound (i); simple phonogram patterns VC (ig)
mat		Consonant sounds (m, t); short vowel sound (a); simple phonogram patterns VC (at)
pet		Consonant sounds (p, t); short vowel sound (e); simple phonogram patterns VC (et)
fun		Consonant sounds (f, n); short vowel sound (u); simple phonogram patterns VC (un)
Kim's		Possessives
wave		Phonogram patterns with a long vowel sound (VCe)
drop		Consonant clusters (dr)
you'll		Contractions (will)
feet		Phonograms with double vowels (VVC)
this		Consonant digraphs (th)
hole		Phonogram patterns with a long vowel sound (VCe)
ant		Short vowel sound (a)
Mom's		Possessives
puppy		Double consonants (middle); multisyllable words
seal		Phonograms with two vowels (VVC)
bedroom		Compound words; multisyllable words
boat		Phonograms with two vowels (VVC)
list		Consonant clusters (st)
pile		Phonogram patterns with a long vowel sound (VCe)
wash		Consonant digraphs (sh)
she's		Contractions (is)
hammer		Double consonants (middle); multisyllable words
race		Phonogram patterns with a long vowel sound (VCe)
jump		Consonant clusters (mp)
I'm		Contractions (am)
kiss		Double consonants (end)
baseball		Compound words; multisyllable words
strip		Consonant clusters (str)
bell		Double consonants (end)
white		Consonant digraphs (wh)

Grade 1 Word Features Test—**Class Record**

| big |
| mat |
| pet |
| fun |
| Kim's |
| wave |
| drop |
| you'll |
| feet |
| this |
| hole |
| ant |
| Mom's |
| puppy |
| seal |
| bedroom |
| boat |
| list |
| pile |
| wash |
| she's |
| hammer |
| race |
| jump |
| I'm |
| kiss |
| baseball |
| strip |
| bell |
| white |

Grade 2 Word Features Test

Description　Children read 30 words, which include a variety of features.

You Need
▶ Grade 2 Word Features List

▶ Grade 2 Word Features Test—Individual Record form

▶ Grade 2 Word Features Test—Class Record form

Why Use It　This assessment will give you information about which features of words children are able to attend to. The substitutions they make will also provide information about their knowledge of letter/sound relationships, spelling patterns, and word structure.

How to Use It
▶ Administer this assessment individually.

▶ Ask the child to read down the list of 30 words.

▶ On the Individual Record form, record the child's correct responses as well as substitutions.

What to Notice
▶ Word features the child can read correctly

▶ Word features with which the child has difficulty

Grade 2 Word Features List

Read the words:

Jack's	my	fish
need	loud	I've
tiger	remake	treat
knit	spy	replay
save	fast	know
I'll	comb	banana
umbrella	mule	scrap
hide	with	don't
lamb	we're	apple
dog's	baby	whale

Grade 2 Word Features Test—**Individual Record**

Name _____ Date _____

Word	✓ or substitution	Feature
Jack's		Possessives
need		Phonograms with double vowels (VVC)
tiger		Multisyllable words, *r*-controlled vowel (er)
knit		Silent consonants (k)
save		Phonogram patterns with a long vowel sound (VCe)
I'll		Contractions (will)
umbrella		Multisyllable words
hide		Phonogram patterns with a long vowel sound (VCe)
lamb		Silent consonants (b)
dog's		Possessives
my		*Y* as a vowel sound
loud		Phonograms with two vowels (VVC)
remake		Prefixes (re); multisyllable words
spy		*Y* as a vowel sound Consonant clusters (sp)
fast		Consonant clusters (st)
comb		Silent consonants (b)
mule		Phonogram patterns with a long vowel sound (VCe)
with		Consonant digraphs (th)
we're		Contractions (are)
baby		*Y* as a vowel sound Multisyllable words
fish		Consonant digraphs (sh)
I've		Contractions (have)
treat		Phonograms with two vowels (VVC) Consonant clusters (tr)
replay		Prefixes (re)
know		Silent consonants (k)
banana		Multisyllable words
scrap		Consonant clusters (scr)
don't		Contractions (not)
apple		Multisyllable words
whale		Consonant digraphs (wh)

Fountas & Pinnell Benchmark Assessment System 1

Grade 2 Word Features Test—**Class Record**

Jack's													
need													
tiger													
knit													
save													
I'll													
umbrella													
hide													
lamb													
dog's													
my													
loud													
remake													
spy													
fast													
comb													
mule													
with													
we're													
baby													
fish													
I've													
treat													
replay													
know													
banana													
scrap													
don't													
apple													
whale													

Grade 3 Word Features Test

Description   Students read 30 words, which include a variety of features.

You Need
▶ Grade 3 Word Features List

▶ Grade 3 Word Features Test—Individual Record form

▶ Grade 3 Word Features Test—Class Record form

Why Use It   This assessment will give you information about which features of words students are able to attend to. The substitutions they make will also provide information about their knowledge of letter/sound relationships, spelling patterns, and word structure.

How to Use It
▶ Administer this assessment individually.

▶ Ask the student to read down the list of 30 words.

▶ On the Individual Record form, record the student's correct responses as well as substitutions.

What to Notice
▶ Word features the student can read correctly

▶ Word features with which the student has difficulty

Grade 3 Word Features List

Read the words:

first	leave	waste
trouble	sunny	we've
bark	untie	remake
passing	homesick	rotten
chair	bird	boy
deer	batter	pie
they'd	corn	driveway
winter	rough	redo
noise	snore	beast
enter	you've	jellyfish

Grade 3 Word Features Test—**Individual Record**

Name _____   Date _____

Word	✓ or substitution	Feature
first		Phonogram patterns in single-syllable words (VCCC)
trouble		Syllable patterns in multisyllable words (ble)
bark		Phonogram patterns in single-syllable words (vowels and r)
passing		Syllable patterns in multisyllable words (VCC pattern, syllable juncture)
chair		Consonant digraph (ch)
deer		Phonogram patterns in single-syllable words (long vowel sound)
they'd		Contractions (would)
winter		Syllable patterns in multisyllable words (in)
noise		Phonogram patterns in single-syllable words (/oy/)
enter		Syllable patterns in multisyllable words (en)
leave		Phonogram patterns in single-syllable words (VVCe)
sunny		Syllable patterns in multisyllable words (un)
untie		Prefixes (un)
homesick		Compound words
bird		Phonogram patterns in single-syllable words (vowels and r)
batter		Syllable patterns in multisyllable words (at)
corn		Phonogram patterns in single-syllable words (vowels and r)
rough		Consonant digraph (gh)
snore		Phonogram patterns in single-syllable words (long vowel sound)
you've		Contractions (have)
waste		Phonogram patterns in single-syllable words (VCCe)
we've		Contractions (have)
remake		Prefixes
rotten		Syllable patterns in multisyllable words (VCC pattern, syllable juncture)
boy		Phonogram patterns in single-syllable words (/oy/)
pie		Phonogram patterns in single-syllable words (long vowel sound)
driveway		Compound words
redo		Prefixes (re)
beast		Phonogram patterns in single-syllable words (VVCC)
jellyfish		Compound words

Grade 3 Word Features Test—**Class Record**

first														
trouble														
bark														
passing														
chair														
deer														
they'd														
winter														
noise														
enter														
leave														
sunny														
untie														
homesick														
bird														
batter														
corn														
rough														
snore														
you've														
waste														
we've														
remake														
rotten														
boy														
pie														
driveway														
redo														
beast														
jellyfish														

Vocabulary Assessments

In this section, you will find a rich array of assessments for identifying students' understanding of word meanings. Use this information in conjunction with the data you gather in the benchmark assessment conferences.

Concept Words–**Number**

Description   Prompted by a picture card, children say the related concept word.

You Need
▶ Numeral and Number Word Cards sheet representing numbers one through twelve

▶ Dot Cards sheet

▶ Concept Words: Numbers and Colors—Class Record form

Why Use It   This assessment will give you information about children's oral vocabulary—that is, the extent to which they know the labels for number concepts. These words help young children read simple texts. Use this assessment to identify areas in which more instruction is needed and to determine which children need more support in developing their number vocabulary.

How to Use It
▶ Gather the three sets of cards: (1) cards with groupings of dots (one through twelve), (2) cards with the numerals 1 through 12, and (3) cards with the number words *one* through *twelve*. (If you think the concepts one through twelve are too difficult for most children, you can reduce the initial task to one through ten or one through five and administer the assessment again later in the year.)

▶ Select one or all of these options:
• • Have children look at the cards with dots and tell you the appropriate quantity.
• • Have children match the cards with dots and the numeral cards.
• • Have children match the cards with dots and the number word cards.
• • Have children read the numerals and words.
• • Have children match the cards with dots, the numeral cards, and the number word cards.

▶ On the Class Record, write the number of correct items and note areas of confusion.

What to Notice
▶ Extent to which the child has developed a concept of number

▶ Ability to recognize and use number words

▶ Number of number words almost known

Dot Cards

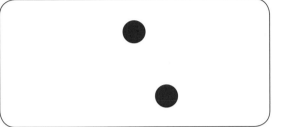
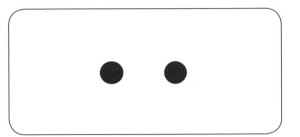
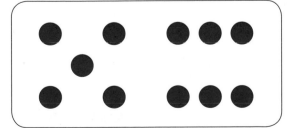

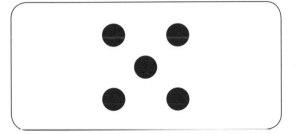

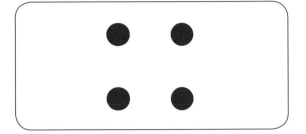
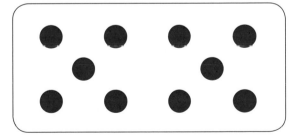
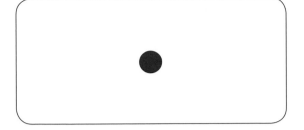

Vocabulary Assessments

Numeral and Number Word Cards

1	2	3
4	5	6
7	8	9
10	11	12
one	two	three
four	five	six
seven	eight	nine
ten	eleven	twelve

Concept Words–**Color**

Description | Prompted by a picture card, children say the related concept word.

You Need
- Color Word Cards sheet
- For the colors *blue*, *yellow*, *orange*, *red*, *green*, *white*, *black*, and *purple*, prepare a set of cards depicting circles or squares in the appropriate color
- Concept Words: Numbers and Colors—Class Record form
- Matching Color Words sheet

Why Use It

This assessment will give you information about children's oral vocabulary—that is, the extent to which they know the labels for color concepts. These words help young children read simple texts. Use this assessment to identify areas in which more instruction is needed and to determine which children need more work in developing their knowledge of color words.

How to Use It
- Have children use the color and word cards to:
  - Say the appropriate color word for each color card.
  - Match the color cards and word cards or color boxes on the word cards with the appropriate color crayon (see the Color Words Matching sheet).
  - Read the word cards.
- Don't be concerned if you see children reading and matching the words printed on the crayons. If they can do this, the assessment is probably not necessary. Also remember that many boys have some degree of color blindness, and adjust your expectations accordingly.
- On the Class Record, write the number of correct items and note areas of confusion.

What to Notice
- Extent to which the child has developed a concept of color
- Ability to recognize and use color words
- Number of color words almost known

Vocabulary Assessments

Color Word Cards

red	green
yellow	blue
black	white
purple	orange

Matching Color Words

Name _____

Color the box.

blue

yellow

orange

red

green

white

black

purple

Vocabulary Assessments

Concept Words: Numbers and Colors—**Class Record**

Date _____

Name	Number Words				Color Words		
	Matches Concept and Word Orally	Matches Concept and Numeral	Matches Concept and Word	Reads Numeral Word	Matches Concept and Word Orally	Matches Concept and Word	Reads Color Word
1.							
2.							
3.							
4.							
5.							
6.							
7.							
8.							
9.							
10.							
11.							
12.							
13.							
14.							
15.							
16.							
17.							
18.							
19.							
20.							
21.							
22.							
23.							
24.							
25.							
26.							
27.							
28.							

Concept Words in Isolation

Description	Children read and talk about a series of concept words: days of the week, seasons of the year, months of the year, weather words, position words (first, second, third, etc.).
You Need	▶ Pocket chart
	▶ Concept Word Cards sheet for days of the week, seasons of the year, months of the year, weather, and position or create your own (in enlarged version if used with pocket chart)
	▶ Concept Words: In Isolation and in Sentences—Class Record form
Why Use It	These assessments will give you information about children's oral and reading vocabularies. It will help you notice the concept words that seem hard for individuals or the group in general to understand. You can use this information to plan future minilessons.
How to Use It	▶ Administer these assessments individually, in a small group, or with the whole class.
	▶ Assemble word cards for concept words that your students will be expected to know (days of the week, seasons of the year, months of the year, weather words, position words).
	▶ Place word cards in the pocket chart. Ask children to try to read some of the words and then ask them what these words mean. After they respond, ask them or cue them as to the category of words, and then ask them to read the words again.
	▶ Over time, accumulate results and enter them on the Class Record.
What to Notice	▶ Slow responses
	▶ Ability to recognize and use specific concept words
	▶ Speed in recognizing words

Vocabulary Assessments

Concept Word Cards

Sunday	Monday	Tuesday
Wednesday	Thursday	Friday
Saturday	January	February
March	April	May
June	July	August
September	October	November
December	winter	spring
summer	fall	sun
clouds	rain	snow
first	second	third

Concept Words in Sentences

Description   Children read sentences that include concept words (days of the week, seasons of the year, months of the year, weather words, etc.), locate the words, and then reread the sentences.

You Need
▶ Sentences that include concept words (select from sample set included or create your own based on children's experiences—Concept Word Sentences sheet)

▶ Concept Words: In Isolation and in Sentences—Class Record form

Why Use It   Many books that children read will feature these concept words. This assessment will give you information about children's ability to locate these words quickly and use them to monitor their reading.

How to Use It
▶ Administer this assessment to individuals or a small group; in a group, have children take turns.

▶ Prepare sets of sentences using concept words, and ask children to read them with you (Shared Reading). Examples of sentences are provided, but you will need to adjust them to fit your own environment.

▶ Then ask the children to locate specific concept words.

▶ Over time, accumulate results and enter them on the Class Record.

What to Notice
▶ The child's ability to locate specific concept words

▶ Number of concept words the child locates accurately

Vocabulary Assessments

Concept Word Sentences

On Monday, I read a book.

On Sunday, I rode my bike.

On Saturday, I went to town.

On Friday, I had pizza.

On Thursday, I played with my friends.

On Wednesday, I went for a walk.

On Tuesday, I baked some cookies.

What did I do Monday?

What did I do Friday?

What did I do Tuesday?

Thirty days has September,

April, June, and November.

February has twenty-eight alone.

All the rest have thirty-one.

Excepting leap year, that's the time,

When February's days are twenty-nine.

What months are missing?

October is a month in the fall.

December means that winter is here.

January is the first month of the year.

In March the wind blows.

In May we know it is spring.

In July and August we go swimming.

There are twelve months in the year.

They are January, February, March, April, May, June, July, August, September, October, November, and December.

First, I wake up.

Second, I get out of bed.

Third, I brush my teeth.

Fourth, I get dressed.

Fifth, I eat breakfast.

Sixth, I put on my coat.

Seventh, I say good-bye to my dad.

Eighth, I get on the bus.

Ninth, I go to school.

Tenth, I say hi to my teacher.

What do I do second?

What do I do sixth?

What do I do tenth?

What do I do first?

What do I do fourth?

There are four seasons in the year,

summer, winter, fall [autumn], and spring.

What do you like to do in summer?

[children respond — make list]

What do you like to do in winter?

[children respond — make list]

What do you like to do in fall [autumn]?

[children respond — make list]

What do you like to do in spring?

[children respond — make list]

Concept Words: In Isolation and in Sentences—**Class Record**

Date _____

Name	Days	Months	Seasons	Position Words	Weather Words
1.					
2.					
3.					
4.					
5.					
6.					
7.					
8.					
9.					
10.					
11.					
12.					
13.					
14.					
15.					
16.					
17.					
18.					
19.					
20.					
21.					
22.					
23.					
24.					
25.					
26.					
27.					
28.					

Vocabulary Assessments

Concept Words

Description Children read concept words and sort them into appropriate categories.

You Need
  ▶ Concept Word Lists (select from sample or create your own)
  ▶ Concept Words—Individual Record form
  ▶ Concept Words—Class Record form

Why Use It You may want to check to see whether your students can read the concept words that they are generally expected to have learned in previous grades. Their ability to read this list will give you a quick check on this area of knowledge.

How to Use It
  ▶ Administer this assessment individually.

  ▶ Begin by reviewing the Concept Word Lists and choose lists appropriate for your children. Included are number words (*one* through *twenty-five*), harder color words, months of the year, weather words, position words (*first, second,* etc.). Some lists include words that are linked conceptually, for example, movement, weather, transportation, and time. These are groups of words that children meet frequently in the informational books they are beginning to read. You may want to look at the content curriculum for your district and identify concepts around which you can create a list of words.

  ▶ Select words that are appropriate. (Looking through books that children are expected to read will help.) You will probably not use all the words on any list.

  ▶ Have the student read each list of words and tell how they are alike.

  ▶ Note the results on the Individual Record. Space is provided for additional categories of concept words of your choosing. You can also record results on the Class Record.

  ▶ As an additional assessment, ask children to locate words in texts during guided, shared, or independent reading.

  ▶ You might also want to ask children to sort words into categories. Write the selected words on word cards, and have children sort in two or three categories.

What to Notice
  ▶ Ability to read specific words in categories
  ▶ Speed in recognizing words in a category
  ▶ Number of words known in each category

Concept Word Lists

Time words	Color words	Weather words	Transportation words
afternoon	aqua	breezy	airplane
AM	beige	brisk	automobile
annual	black	cloudy	boat
century	blue	cold	captain
daily	brick	cool	car
dawn	emerald	drizzle	crew
day	gold	fair	cruise
dusk	golden	hot	drive
evening	grape	lightning	driver
hour	gray	mild	engineer
minute	green	rain	ferry
monthly	lavender	showers	float
month	lime	snow	fly
morning	pink	storm	navigate
night	purple	sunny	passenger
PM	red	sultry	pilot
second	rose	thunder	railroad
sunrise	ruby	thunderstorm	railway
sunset	slate	tornado	sail
twilight	tan	warm	sedan
week	tomato	windy	ship
weekly	turquoise		soar
year	violet		steer
yearly	white		train
	yellow		

Vocabulary Assessments

Concept Word Lists

Action words	Describing words that tell something about a person, place, or thing	Describing words that tell how or how much	Calendar words
come	beautiful	above	January
draw	big	around	February
go	dark	before	March
jump	flat	below	April
paint	hard	fast	May
read	light	happily	June
run	little	quickly	July
say	pretty	really	August
sprint	round	sadly	September
stand	short	slowly	October
walk	smooth	stubbornly	November
write	soft	very	December
	square		day
	strong		week
	weak		month
			year

Concept Word Lists

Motion words	Number words	Ordinal words
crawl	one	first
fly	two	second
dance	three	third
gallop	four	fourth
glide	five	fifth
hop	six	sixth
jump	seven	seventh
leap	eight	eighth
roll	nine	ninth
run	ten	tenth
saunter	eleven	eleventh
skate	twelve	twelfth
skip	thirteen	thirteenth
slide	fourteen	fourteenth
soar	fifteen	fifteenth
sprint	sixteen	sixteenth
stroll	seventeen	seventeenth
trot	eighteen	eighteenth
tumble	nineteen	nineteenth
walk	twenty	twentieth
	twenty-one	
	twenty-two	
	twenty-three	
	twenty-four	
	twenty-five	

Vocabulary Assessments

Concept Words—**Individual Record**

Reading Category Words (Word Lists)

Category Word	Check ✓ If Read Accurately
Time words	/24
Color words	/25
Weather words	/21
Transportation words	/24
Action words	/12
Describing words (List # _____)	/15
Describing words (List # _____)	/12
TOTAL	/

Reading Concept Words (Word Lists)

Content Area—Concept Words	Check ✓ If Read Accurately
Calendar words	/16
Motion words	/20
Number words	/25
Ordinal words	/20
TOTAL	/

Understanding Categories of Concept Words (Word Sorts)

Date	Type of Sort (categories)	Check ✓ if Successfully Sorted Words	Notes

Concept Words—**Class Record**

Directions: Check ✓ if student demonstrates an understanding of each set of concept words.

Name	Time	Color	Weather	Transportation	Action	Describes Nouns	Describes How Much	Calendar	Motion	Number	Ordinal

Vocabulary Assessments

Synonyms I

Description   Children locate words that mean the same or about the same as words read by the teacher.

You Need
▶ Synonyms I Word Cards sheet

▶ Synonyms I Assessment—Class Record form

Why Use It   These quick oral assessments will help you know whether students understand the concept of synonyms in their listening and speaking vocabularies.

How to Use It
▶ Administer this assessment orally, either individually or with the whole class.

▶ Say the word pairs one after the other while you hold up the cards. If working with one child, ask her to clap when the two words mean the same or about the same. If working with the whole group, ask children to raise their hands when the two words mean the same or about the same.

▶ As an alternative, have children match pairs of synonym word cards.

▶ Enter the results on the Class Record.

What to Notice
▶ Number of word pairs a child can identify correctly

▶ A child's understanding of the concept of synonym

▶ The specific synonyms a child knows

Synonyms I **Word Cards**

big	large	begin
start	close	shut
little	small	quit
stop	keep	save
call	yell	grab
take	jump	leap
ask	question	own
have	mean	cruel
happy	glad	below
under	end	finish

Vocabulary Assessments

Synonyms I Assessment—**Class Record**

Directions: Place a check mark in the box when the child correctly identifies the synonym.

Name	big/large	begin/start	close/shut	little/small	quit/stop	keep/save	call/yell	grab/take	jump/leap	ask/question	own/have	mean/cruel	happy/glad	below/under	end/finish

Synonyms II

Description   Children read and identify words that mean the same or almost the same thing.

You Need
▷ Synonyms II Word Cards sheet

▷ Synonyms II Assessment—Class Record form

Why Use It   This quick oral assessment will tell you whether the children understand the concept of synonym. Once this concept is understood, you can make a continuous list of synonyms, adding to it throughout the year, for children to refer to during word study, reading, and writing. Work with children who need help in small groups.

How to Use It
▷ Administer this assessment individually or to the whole class. (Individually test children who do not seem to be responding successfully.)

▷ Hold up pairs of word cards, some that are synonyms and some that are not. Ask children to clap or raise their hands when the two words mean about the same. (Examples: *baby, infant; fix, mend; fetch, get; divide, split; near, close; quiet, silent.*)

▷ Enter the results on the Class Record form.

What to Notice
▷ Child's understanding that there are words that can mean almost the same thing

▷ Number of words the child can read accurately

▷ Number of synonym pairs the child can form accurately

▷ Specific synonyms a child understands

Vocabulary Assessments

Synonyms II **Word Cards**

baby	infant	back
rear	change	swap
city	town	divide
split	error	mistake
fetch	get	fix
mend	giant	huge
gift	present	pick
choose	messy	sloppy
near	close	quiet
silent	above	over

Synonyms II Assessment—**Class Record**

Directions: Record the number of synonym pairs that each child correctly identified.

Name	Score of correctly identified synonym pairs	Notes
	/15	
	/15	
	/15	
	/15	
	/15	
	/15	
	/15	
	/15	
	/15	
	/15	
	/15	
	/15	
	/15	
	/15	
	/15	
	/15	
	/15	
	/15	
	/15	
	/15	
	/15	
	/15	
	/15	
	/15	
	/15	
	/15	

Antonyms I

Description Children read and identify words that mean the opposite or almost the opposite as words read by the teacher.

You Need
▶ Antonyms I Word Cards

▶ Antonyms I Assessment—Class Record form

Why Use It These quick oral assessments will help you know whether students understand the concept of antonyms in their listening and speaking vocabularies.

How to Use It
▶ Administer this assessment orally, either individually or with the whole class.

▶ Say the word pairs one after the other while you hold up the cards. If working with one child, ask her to clap when the two words mean the opposite or almost the opposite. If working with the whole group, ask children to raise their hand when the two words mean the opposite or almost the opposite.

▶ As an alternative, have children match pairs of antonym word cards.

▶ Enter the results on the Class Record.

What to Notice
▶ Number of word pairs a child can identify correctly

▶ A child's understanding of the concept of antonym

▶ Specific antonyms a child knows

Antonyms | **Word Cards**

on	off	up
down	in	out
long	short	buy
sell	hot	cold
low	high	big
little	open	close
asleep	awake	laugh
cry	old	young
stop	go	slow
fast	work	play

Vocabulary Assessments

Antonyms I Assessment—**Class Record**

Directions: Place a check mark in the box when the child correctly identifies the antonym.

Names	on/off	up/down	in/out	long/short	buy/sell	hot/cold	low/high	big/little	open/close	asleep/awake	laugh/cry	old/young	stop/go	slow/fast	work/play

Antonyms II

Description Children read and identify words that mean the opposite or almost the opposite.

You Need
- ▶ Antonyms II Word Cards sheet
- ▶ Antonyms II Assessment—Class Record form

Why Use It This quick oral assessment will tell you whether children understand the concept of antonym. Once this concept is understood, you can make a continuous list of antonyms, adding to it throughout the year, for children to refer to during word study, reading, and writing. Work with children who need help in small groups.

How to Use It
- ▶ Administer this assessment individually or to the whole class. (Individually test children who do not seem to be responding successfully.)
- ▶ Hold up pairs of words, some that are antonyms and some that are not. Ask children to clap or raise their hands when the two words mean the opposite.
- ▶ Enter the results on the Class Record.

What to Notice
- ▶ Child's understanding that there are words that mean the opposite
- ▶ Number of words the child can read accurately
- ▶ Number of antonym pairs the child can form accurately
- ▶ Specific antonyms a child knows

Vocabulary Assessments

Antonyms II **Word Cards**

above	below	dark
light	dirty	clean
top	bottom	ask
tell	hard	soft
front	back	empty
full	heavy	light
enemy	friend	loose
tight	shallow	deep
rich	poor	push
pull	smooth	rough

Antonyms II Assessment—**Class Record**

Directions: Record the number of antonym pairs that each child correctly identified.

Name	Score of correctly identified antonym pairs	Notes
	/15	
	/15	
	/15	
	/15	
	/15	
	/15	
	/15	
	/15	
	/15	
	/15	
	/15	
	/15	
	/15	
	/15	
	/15	
	/15	
	/15	
	/15	
	/15	
	/15	
	/15	
	/15	
	/15	
	/15	
	/15	
	/15	
	/15	
	/15	
	/15	

Vocabulary Assessments

Homophones I

Description   Children listen to a sentence and circle the word (homophone) that has the right meaning in the sentence.

You Need   ▶ Student Homophone Sheet

▶ Sentences with Homophones sheet

▶ Homophones I Assessment—Class Record form

Why Use It   Homophones can be very difficult for children. This assessment will help you identify those homophones they know and understand as well as those they do not know. Remember that children will continue learning about homophones and their use throughout elementary school; this assessment presents some of the easiest ones. Children will also be able to get the correct answers partly because they will notice that they can eliminate one of each pair once it is used. In other words, the answer to one homonym pair serves as a check on the other. Do not be concerned that this process makes the assessment too easy. You are gaining information about children's understanding of homophone pairs.

How to Use It   ▶ Give this assessment to the whole class.

▶ Give children the Student Homophone Sheet and read over the list with them. You may want to divide this list into sets of 5–10 homophones rather than giving them all 27 at once.

▶ Remind children that these words sound the same but are spelled differently and have different meanings. You can tell which word to use by listening to the sentence and thinking about what the word means.

▶ Read one sentence to the children and have them circle the correct word. Then have them listen to the sentence with each item and circle the word.

▶ Keep the sheet as the child's individual record. Enter the results on the Class Record form.

What to Notice   ▶ Number of homophones the child can use accurately

▶ Specific homophones the child can read and understand

▶ Understanding the concept of a homophone

Student Homophone Sheet

Name _____ Date _____

Directions: Circle the word you hear in the sentence.

1.	to two too
2.	to two too
3.	to two too
4.	be bee
5.	be bee
6.	their there
7.	their there
8.	I eye
9.	I eye
10.	blue blew
11.	blue blew
12.	our hour
13.	our hour
14.	dear deer

15.	dear deer
16.	ate eight
17.	ate eight
18.	your you're
19.	your you're
20.	no know
21.	no know
22.	read red
23.	read red
24.	see sea
25.	see sea
26.	one won
27.	one won

Vocabulary Assessments

Sentences with Homophones

1. I want cookies, <u>too</u>.
2. The children have to go <u>to</u> school.
3. I have <u>two</u> trucks.
4. The <u>bee</u> landed on the flower.
5. Will you <u>be</u> my friend?
6. I want to go to <u>their</u> house.
7. Will she be <u>there</u> tomorrow?
8. <u>I</u> like to sing songs.
9. You can wink with your <u>eye</u>.
10. The sky is <u>blue</u>.
11. The wind <u>blew</u> the tree down.
12. We like <u>our</u> house.
13. We walked for an <u>hour</u>.
14. <u>Dear</u> friend, please come to my house.
15. I saw a <u>deer</u> leap across our yard.
16. I <u>ate</u> some french fries at the fair.
17. I saw <u>eight</u> birds fly by.
18. This is <u>your</u> book bag.
19. <u>You're</u> going to come with us, aren't you?
20. I <u>know</u> that boy.
21. <u>No</u>, don't do that.
22. I <u>read</u> two books yesterday.
23. I have new <u>red</u> sneakers.
24. I <u>see</u> the dog in the yard.
25. I sailed in a boat on the <u>sea</u>.
26. I have <u>one</u> sandwich.
27. She <u>won</u> the race.

Homophones I Assessment—**Class Record**

Directions: Place a check mark in the box when the child correctly identifies the homophone.

Names	to/too/two	be/bee	their/there	I/eye	blew/blue	our/hour	deer/dear	ate/eight	your/you're	no/know	read/red	see/sea	one/won	Total

Vocabulary Assessments

Homophones II

Description   Children read a sentence and write the correct homophone in the blank space. They choose from two or three words.

You Need
- ▸ Homophones II Lists 1, 2, and 3
- ▸ Homophones II Assessment—Class Record form

Why Use It   Homophones are a challenge for many children, and confusions about them often persist into adulthood. This assessment will give you information about children's ability to use sentence context and meaning to choose the word that matches the meaning. Like adult spellers, children will be partially using a "process of elimination" strategy; that is, if they know one of the homophones, then it is easier to use it or eliminate it. You will have information about the extent to which children understand the principle that words can sound the same but be spelled differently and have different meanings. You can also identify homophones that are particularly difficult for many children, and you may want to address these in lessons.

How to Use It
- ▸ Administer this assessment individually or as a whole group.

- ▸ Using one of the Homophones II Lists provided, children read the sentence and think about which word will fit. They write the word in the blank space. If you have limited time, you may want children simply to circle the correct word. You may want to do a couple of examples with children so that they understand the task. You can also make the examples more accessible by reading down the list of homophones in the right columns so that children hear them before beginning the assessment.

- ▸ Record the results on the Class Record. Expect a fairly high score on this assessment to determine whether children understand the principle. (Remember that by guessing, children may still get many answers right.) If you can, observe children while they are working. You can note from their behavior whether they are simply guessing or carefully considering the meaning of the words.

What to Notice
- ▸ Number of homophones children correctly represent in sentence context

- ▸ Ease with which children perform the task

- ▸ Particular homophones that children can read and understand

- ▸ Particular homophones that children find difficult

Homophones II **List 1**

Name _____ Date _____

Directions: Write the word in the sentence. Choose the correct one from the words on the right.

---

1. I _____ she would arrive late.

new
knew

---

2. When you make bread, you might use _____.

flour
flower

---

3. My _____ sent me a card for my birthday.

ant
aunt

---

4. Can you tell me the _____ to New York?

way
weigh

---

5. The girl shouted, " _____, guys!" to the boys.

Hay
Hey

---

6. I _____ my bike to my friend's house.

road
rode
rowed

---

7. I ate the _____ salad.

hole
whole

---

8. This desk has nothing on it. It is _____.

bear
bare

---

9. Everyone is going to _____ at the new statue.

stair
stare

---

10. When you add the numbers you get the _____.

some
sum

Vocabulary Assessments

11. My grandmother taught me to _____.

    sew
    so

12. _____ going to be late for class.

    Your
    You're

13. I will _____ someone to help me with the work.

    higher
    hire

14. Speak loudly so I can _____ you.

    hear
    here

15. My mom is buying me _____ today.

    close
    clothes

16. My brother has a _____ named William.

    son
    sun

17. _____ you like to go to the movies tonight?

    Wood
    Would

18. They took _____ dogs for a nice long walk.

    their
    there

19. I saw a _____ hop over the rock.

    hair
    hare

20. _____ shirt do you like better?

    Which
    Witch

Homophones II **List 2**

Name _____ Date _____

Directions: Write the word in the sentence. Choose the correct one from the words on the right.

---

1. I lost the _____ of my left shoe.

    heal
    heel
    he'll

---

2. The weather had a big _____ on the game.

    affect
    effect

---

3. When you want to stop the car, put on the _____.

    break
    brake

---

4. The school _____ asked all the teachers to come to the meeting.

    principal
    principle

---

5. He _____ how to make model airplanes.

    knows
    nose

---

6. "I'm so tired," she _____.

    side
    sighed

---

7. In this game, you throw the _____ to move your marker.

    die
    dye

---

8. I hope I can _____ the earrings I lost.

    find
    fined

---

9. To make cookies, you must first make the _____.

    doe
    dough

---

10. The toy was on sale. It was _____.

    cheap
    cheep

---

11. Would you like to _____ a new book to read?   chews
choose

12. He walked down the _____ at the grocery store.   aisle
I'll
isle

13. The truck will _____ the trash away.   hall
haul

14. The postman dropped off the _____.   male
mail

15. I _____ a letter to my pen pal.   cent
sent
scent

16. James was so _____ that he went to sleep.   board
bored

17. I like _____ pasta with sauce.   plain
plane

18. Do you _____ passing the potatoes?   mind
mined

19. My little sister _____ a cold.   caught
cot

20. The _____ for the bus is one dollar.   fair
fare

Homophones II **List 3**

Name _____ Date _____

Directions: Write the word in the sentence. Choose the correct one from the words on the right.

1. Everyone came to the game, _____ for Don, who was out of town.

   accept
   except

2. During the storm, we saw some _____.

   hail
   hale

3. Hannah _____ the answer to the question.

   guest
   guessed

4. There is a _____ in the roof, and the rain is coming in.

   leak
   leek

5. My old chair would _____ whenever I sat in it.

   creak
   creek

6. On a cold morning, you can sometimes see _____ on the grass.

   dew
   due
   do

7. There is a _____ of sheep on the hill.

   heard
   herd

8. I told the plumber we need _____ to come right now.

   him
   hymn

9. My voice is _____ from cheering at the concert.

   hoarse
   horse

10. The baker will _____ the dough to make the bread.

    knead
    need

Vocabulary Assessments

11. I _____ my bed every morning this week.

made
maid

12. I _____ want to have another slice of pizza.

might
mite

13. The storm forced the people to _____ to higher ground.

flea
flee

14. A chicken is a _____.

foul
fowl

15. You use the _____ to make a horse stop.

rain
reign
rein

16. When you wash something, you will want to _____ out the water.

ring
wring

17. It is very important to water the _____ of the plant.

root
route

18. The store was having a big _____.

sale
sail

19. The boys said that the game was not _____.

fare
fair

20. The choir sang a beautiful _____.

hymn
him

Homophones II Assessment—**Class Record**

Directions: Record the number of homophones that each child correctly identified.

Name	List 1	List 2	List 3
	/20	/20	/20
	/20	/20	/20
	/20	/20	/20
	/20	/20	/20
	/20	/20	/20
	/20	/20	/20
	/20	/20	/20
	/20	/20	/20
	/20	/20	/20
	/20	/20	/20
	/20	/20	/20
	/20	/20	/20
	/20	/20	/20
	/20	/20	/20
	/20	/20	/20
	/20	/20	/20
	/20	/20	/20
	/20	/20	/20
	/20	/20	/20
	/20	/20	/20
	/20	/20	/20
	/20	/20	/20
	/20	/20	/20
	/20	/20	/20
	/20	/20	/20
	/20	/20	/20
	/20	/20	/20

Vocabulary Assessments

Vocabulary in Context

Description   Children use context to correctly identify the meaning of words from a Benchmark Assessment Book at their Instructional Level or Independent Level.

You Need   ▶ The Benchmark Assessment Book at the child's Instructional Level or Independent Level.

▶ Assessing Vocabulary in Context—Individual Record form for the corresponding Benchmark Assessment Book.

Why Use It   As they read continuous text, readers constantly face vocabulary challenges. Many words they already know and can link to the array of letters that make up the word in print. Others may be new or only partially known. In this case, the reader derives the meaning from the context, and this ability is a key factor in comprehension. Often words have two or three alternative meanings. The reader must know precisely which definition is being used in a given text. This assessment will enable you to measure the student's knowledge of vocabulary as well as her ability to derive the precise meaning of words in the context of a short book.

How to Use It   ▶ Choosing either the student's Instructional Level book or Independent Level book (or both), select words from the list on the corresponding Individual Record, checking those that you used.

▶ For each word, have the student turn to the page where the word appears. Then ask: "What does [word] mean in this book?"

▶ Score the student's answers using the following rubric:

0	Did not respond or said "I don't know"
1	Made a response that is in some way related to the meaning of the word (any definition of that word)
2	Responded with a definition that is approximately the meaning of the word (same definition of the word as used in the text)
3	Responded with a full definition of the word (precise definition used in the text)

▶ Using the chart below, determine whether the student's Vocabulary in Context score is Unsatisfactory, Satisfactory, or Excellent.

Level	Unsatisfactory	Satisfactory	Excellent
A, B, C	0–4	5–6	7–9
D, E, F, G	0–6	7–8	9–12
H, I, J, K, L, M, N	0–8	9–11	12–15

▶ Circle the rubric according to the total score.

What to Notice   ▶ Number of words known or almost known

▶ Student's use of context to determine which meaning of a word is appropriate

Assessing Vocabulary in Context: Level A, Fiction
Individual Record

Name _____ Grade _____ Date _____

Best Friends

Check ✓ one: Instructional Level: _____   Independent Level: _____

Vocabulary Word (✓ 3 Words Selected)		Meaning	Student Response
	dance, p. 4	To move your body, usually to music	0 1 2 3
	climb, p. 8	To move upward, often pulling with your hands to help you move	0 1 2 3
	slide, p. 10	To move smoothly down the surface of a piece of playground equipment	0 1 2 3
	paint, p. 14	To cover something with color	0 1 2 3
		Total Score	

Score:

0 Did not respond or said "I don't know"

1 Made a response that is in some way related to the meaning of the word (any definition of that word)

2 Responded with a definition that is approximately the meaning of the word (same definition of the word as used in the text)

3 Responded with a full definition of the word (precise definition used in the text)

Level	Unsatisfactory	Satisfactory	Excellent
A, B, C	0–4	5–6	7–9
D, E, F, G	0–6	7–8	9–12
H, I, J, K, L, M, N	0–8	9–11	12–15

▶ Circle the rubric according to the total score.

Vocabulary Assessments

Assessing Vocabulary in Context: Level A, Nonfiction
Individual Record

Name _____   Grade _____   Date _____

At the Park

Check ✓ one: Instructional Level: _____   Independent Level: _____

Vocabulary Word (✓ 3 Words Selected)		Meaning	Student Response
	catch, p. 6	To get hold of something that is in the air	0 1 2 3
	jump, p. 8	To launch yourself into the air	0 1 2 3
	swing, p. 10	To move forward and backward while sitting on a hanging seat	0 1 2 3
	slide, p. 12	To move smoothly down the surface of a piece of playground equipment	0 1 2 3
		Total Score	

Score:

0 Did not respond or said "I don't know"

1 Made a response that is in some way related to the meaning of the word (any definition of that word)

2 Responded with a definition that is approximately the meaning of the word (same definition of the word as used in the text)

3 Responded with a full definition of the word (precise definition used in the text)

Level	Unsatisfactory	Satisfactory	Excellent
A, B, C	0–4	5–6	7–9
D, E, F, G	0–6	7–8	9–12
H, I, J, K, L, M, N	0–8	9–11	12–15

▶ Circle the rubric according to the total score.

Assessing Vocabulary in Context: Level B, Fiction
Individual Record

Name _____ Grade _____ Date _____

My Little Dog

Check ✓ one: Instructional Level: _____ Independent Level: _____

Vocabulary Word (✓ 3 Words Selected)		Meaning	Student Response
	sleep, p. 2	To rest your mind and body with your eyes closed	0 1 2 3
	eat, p. 4	To take in food by chewing and swallowing it	0 1 2 3
	play, p. 8	To take part in a game or activity, usually with others	0 1 2 3
	ride, p. 10	To sit on or control something that moves	0 1 2 3
	read, p. 14	To understand written words	0 1 2 3
		Total Score	

Score:

0 Did not respond or said "I don't know"

1 Made a response that is in some way related to the meaning of the word (any definition of that word)

2 Responded with a definition that is approximately the meaning of the word (same definition of the word as used in the text)

3 Responded with a full definition of the word (precise definition used in the text)

Level	Unsatisfactory	Satisfactory	Excellent
A, B, C	0–4	5–6	7–9
D, E, F, G	0–6	7–8	9–12
H, I, J, K, L, M, N	0–8	9–11	12–15

▶ Circle the rubric according to the total score.

Vocabulary Assessments

Assessing Vocabulary in Context: Level B, Nonfiction
Individual Record

Name _____ Grade _____ Date _____

Playing

Check ✓ one: Instructional Level: _____   Independent Level: _____

Vocabulary Word (✓ 3 Words Selected)		Meaning	Student Response
	car, p. 4	A vehicle with an engine and wheels that is used to move a small number of people from one place to another	0 1 2 3
	doll, p. 8	A toy that is made to look like a person	0 1 2 3
	train, p. 10	A vehicle with an engine that usually pulls a number of cars, runs on tracks, and carries people or things from one place to another	0 1 2 3
	plane, p. 12	A vehicle that can fly and carries people or things from one place to another	0 1 2 3
	boat, p. 14	A vehicle that floats in the water and carries people or things from one place to another	0 1 2 3
		Total Score	

Score:

0 Did not respond or said "I don't know"

1 Made a response that is in some way related to the meaning of the word (any definition of that word)

2 Responded with a definition that is approximately the meaning of the word (same definition of the word as used in the text)

3 Responded with a full definition of the word (precise definition used in the text)

Level	Unsatisfactory	Satisfactory	Excellent
A, B, C	0–4	5–6	7–9
D, E, F, G	0–6	7–8	9–12
H, I, J, K, L, M, N	0–8	9–11	12–15

▶ Circle the rubric according to the total score.

Assessing Vocabulary in Context: Level C, Fiction
Individual Record

Name _____   Grade _____   Date _____

Socks

Check ✓ one: Instructional Level: _____   Independent Level: _____

Vocabulary Word (✓ 3 Words Selected)		Meaning	Student Response
	wake, p. 2	To stop sleeping	0 1 2 3
	couch, p. 6	A piece of furniture that you can sit or lie on	0 1 2 3
	window, p. 10	An opening in a wall that lets in light and air	0 1 2 3
	under, p. 14	Below or beneath	0 1 2 3
		Total Score	

Score:

0 Did not respond or said "I don't know"

1 Made a response that is in some way related to the meaning of the word (any definition of that word)

2 Responded with a definition that is approximately the meaning of the word (same definition of the word as used in the text)

3 Responded with a full definition of the word (precise definition used in the text)

Level	Unsatisfactory	Satisfactory	Excellent
A, B, C	0–4	5–6	7–9
D, E, F, G	0–6	7–8	9–12
H, I, J, K, L, M, N	0–8	9–11	12–15

▶ Circle the rubric according to the total score.

Vocabulary Assessments

Assessing Vocabulary in Context: Level C, Nonfiction
Individual Record

Name _____   Grade _____   Date _____

Shopping

Check ✓ one: Instructional Level: _____   Independent Level: _____

Vocabulary Word (✓ 3 Words Selected)		Meaning	Student Response
	apples, p. 4	A red fruit with a thin skin that can be eaten	0 1 2 3
	oranges, p. 8	A fruit with a thick skin that must be peeled off before eating the inside	0 1 2 3
	bread, p. 14	A food made with flour and other ingredients and baked in an oven; it is often cut into slices	0 1 2 3
	cookies, p. 16	Small, sweet-tasting cakes	0 1 2 3
		Total Score	

Score:

0 Did not respond or said "I don't know"

1 Made a response that is in some way related to the meaning of the word (any definition of that word)

2 Responded with a definition that is approximately the meaning of the word (same definition of the word as used in the text)

3 Responded with a full definition of the word (precise definition used in the text)

Level	Unsatisfactory	Satisfactory	Excellent
A, B, C	0–4	5–6	7–9
D, E, F, G	0–6	7–8	9–12
H, I, J, K, L, M, N	0–8	9–11	12–15

▶ Circle the rubric according to the total score.

Assessing Vocabulary in Context: Level D, Fiction
Individual Record

Name _____ Grade _____ Date _____

The Nice Little House

Check ✓ one: Instructional Level: _____   Independent Level: _____

Vocabulary Word (✓ 4 Words Selected)		Meaning	Student Response
	horse, p. 2	A large animal that is often used to pull things or to ride on	0 1 2 3
	little, p. 2	Small in size	0 1 2 3
	nice, p. 2	Pleasant or good	0 1 2 3
	chicken, p. 8	A kind of bird, often used to lay eggs for humans to eat	0 1 2 3
	duck, p. 10	A water bird with a wide, flat beak (called a bill) and webbed feet	0 1 2 3
	skunk, p. 12	A bad-smelling animal with black and white fur	0 1 2 3
		Total Score	

Score:

0 Did not respond or said "I don't know"

1 Made a response that is in some way related to the meaning of the word (any definition of that word)

2 Responded with a definition that is approximately the meaning of the word (same definition of the word as used in the text)

3 Responded with a full definition of the word (precise definition used in the text)

Level	Unsatisfactory	Satisfactory	Excellent
A, B, C	0–4	5–6	7–9
D, E, F, G	0–6	7–8	9–12
H, I, J, K, L, M, N	0–8	9–11	12–15

▶ Circle the rubric according to the total score.

Assessing Vocabulary in Context: Level D, Nonfiction
Individual Record

Name _____ Grade _____ Date _____

Our Teacher Mr. Brown

Check ✓ one: Instructional Level: _____   Independent Level: _____

Vocabulary Word (✓ 4 Words Selected)		Meaning	Student Response
	teacher, p. 2	A person who helps others learn about things	0 1 2 3
	write, p. 6	To make letters or words	0 1 2 3
	read, p. 6	To say written words aloud	0 1 2 3
	books, p. 8	Pages with words on them, collected together with a cover	0 1 2 3
	paint, p. 10	To cover a surface with colorful liquid	0 1 2 3
	draw, p. 10	To make a picture of something with a pen, a pencil, or any writing tool	0 1 2 3
		Total Score	

Score:

0 Did not respond or said "I don't know"

1 Made a response that is in some way related to the meaning of the word (any definition of that word)

2 Responded with a definition that is approximately the meaning of the word (same definition of the word as used in the text)

3 Responded with a full definition of the word (precise definition used in the text)

Level	Unsatisfactory	Satisfactory	Excellent
A, B, C	0–4	5–6	7–9
D, E, F, G	0–6	7–8	9–12
H, I, J, K, L, M, N	0–8	9–11	12–15

▶ Circle the rubric according to the total score.

Assessing Vocabulary in Context: Level E, Fiction
Individual Record

Name _____ Grade _____ Date _____

The Loose Tooth

Check ✓ one: Instructional Level: _____   Independent Level: _____

Vocabulary Word (✓ 4 Words Selected)		Meaning	Student Response
	loose, p. 2	Not held in place well; not tight	0 1 2 3
	very, p. 2	Extremely; to a large degree; a lot	0 1 2 3
	breakfast, p. 4	The first meal of the day, eaten in the morning	0 1 2 3
	wiggled, p. 5	Moved back and forth	0 1 2 3
	lunch, p. 10	The meal eaten in the middle of the day	0 1 2 3
	soup, p. 13	A liquid food, usually with vegetables or meats in it	0 1 2 3
	bite, p. 15	A piece of food that is taken by the mouth from a larger piece of food	0 1 2 3
		Total Score	

Score:

0   Did not respond or said "I don't know"

1   Made a response that is in some way related to the meaning of the word (any definition of that word)

2   Responded with a definition that is approximately the meaning of the word (same definition of the word as used in the text)

3   Responded with a full definition of the word (precise definition used in the text)

Level	Unsatisfactory	Satisfactory	Excellent
A, B, C	0–4	5–6	7–9
D, E, F, G	0–6	7–8	9–12
H, I, J, K, L, M, N	0–8	9–11	12–15

▶ Circle the rubric according to the total score.

Vocabulary Assessments

Assessing Vocabulary in Context: Level E, Nonfiction
Individual Record

Name _____ Grade _____ Date _____

The Zoo

Check ✓ one: Instructional Level: _____   Independent Level: _____

Vocabulary Word (✓ 4 Words Selected)		Meaning	Student Response
	elephant, p. 2	A very large animal with big ears and a trunk	0 1 2 3
	polar bears, p. 6	Large, white animals that live in very cold places	0 1 2 3
	fur, p. 6	A soft, hairy covering that some animals have on their bodies	0 1 2 3
	lions, p. 8	Large animals that belong to the cat family	0 1 2 3
	giraffes, p. 10	Animals with very long necks	0 1 2 3
	penguins, p. 12	Black and white birds that live in cold places and cannot fly	0 1 2 3
	chimps, p. 14	Animals that live in forests and are related to apes	0 1 2 3
		Total Score	

Score:

0   Did not respond or said "I don't know"

1   Made a response that is in some way related to the meaning of the word (any definition of that word)

2   Responded with a definition that is approximately the meaning of the word (same definition of the word as used in the text)

3   Responded with a full definition of the word (precise definition used in the text)

Level	Unsatisfactory	Satisfactory	Excellent
A, B, C	0–4	5–6	7–9
D, E, F, G	0–6	7–8	9–12
H, I, J, K, L, M, N	0–8	9–11	12–15

▶ Circle the rubric according to the total score.

Assessing Vocabulary in Context: Level F, Fiction
Individual Record

Name _____ Grade _____ Date _____

Anna's New Glasses

Check ✓ one: Instructional Level: _____   Independent Level: _____

Vocabulary Word (✓ 4 Words Selected)		Meaning	Student Response
	ready, p. 2	Able to start; prepared	0 1 2 3
	school, p. 2	A place where people go to learn	0 1 2 3
	backpack, p. 2	A bag worn on the back, with straps that go on the shoulders	0 1 2 3
	glasses, p. 2	A frame with lenses, worn on the face to help someone see better	0 1 2 3
	doctor, p. 6	A person who is trained to help sick or injured people get better	0 1 2 3
	great, p. 11	Good; special	0 1 2 3
		Total Score	

Score:

0 Did not respond or said "I don't know"

1 Made a response that is in some way related to the meaning of the word (any definition of that word)

2 Responded with a definition that is approximately the meaning of the word (same definition of the word as used in the text)

3 Responded with a full definition of the word (precise definition used in the text)

Level	Unsatisfactory	Satisfactory	Excellent
A, B, C	0–4	5–6	7–9
D, E, F, G	0–6	7–8	9–12
H, I, J, K, L, M, N	0–8	9–11	12–15

▶ Circle the rubric according to the total score.

Vocabulary Assessments

Assessing Vocabulary in Context: Level F, Nonfiction
Individual Record

Name _____ Grade _____ Date _____

From Nest to Bird

Check ✓ one: Instructional Level: _____   Independent Level: _____

Vocabulary Word (✓ 4 Words Selected)		Meaning	Student Response
	sticks, p. 3	Small branches broken off from trees	0 1 2 3
	grass, p. 3	Plants with long, skinny leaves	0 1 2 3
	nest, p. 3	Something a bird makes to keep its eggs safe and warm	0 1 2 3
	eggs, p. 5	Round objects produced by some female animals that have a baby animal inside	0 1 2 3
	warm, p. 7	A temperature between cold and hot	0 1 2 3
	bugs, p. 11	Small animals that creep and crawl; insects	0 1 2 3
		Total Score	

Score:

0 Did not respond or said "I don't know"

1 Made a response that is in some way related to the meaning of the word (any definition of that word)

2 Responded with a definition that is approximately the meaning of the word (same definition of the word as used in the text)

3 Responded with a full definition of the word (precise definition used in the text)

Level	Unsatisfactory	Satisfactory	Excellent
A, B, C	0–4	5–6	7–9
D, E, F, G	0–6	7–8	9–12
H, I, J, K, L, M, N	0–8	9–11	12–15

▶ Circle the rubric according to the total score.

Assessing Vocabulary in Context: Level G, Fiction
Individual Record

Name _____ Grade _____ Date _____

Bedtime for Nick

Check ✓ one: Instructional Level: _____   Independent Level: _____

Vocabulary Word (✓ 4 Words Selected)		Meaning	Student Response
	pajamas, p. 4	Clothes worn to bed	0 1 2 3
	washed, p. 4	Cleaned, with soap and water	0 1 2 3
	brushed, p. 4	Scrubbed in order to clean	0 1 2 3
	over, p. 6	Finished; done; completed	0 1 2 3
	nightlight, p. 8	A small light that is left on at night when other lights are turned off	0 1 2 3
	open, p. 12	To change from a shut or closed position	0 1 2 3
	missing, p. 14	Absent; not present; lost	0 1 2 3
		Total Score	

Score:

0 Did not respond or said "I don't know"

1 Made a response that is in some way related to the meaning of the word (any definition of that word)

2 Responded with a definition that is approximately the meaning of the word (same definition of the word as used in the text)

3 Responded with a full definition of the word (precise definition used in the text)

Level	Unsatisfactory	Satisfactory	Excellent
A, B, C	0–4	5–6	7–9
D, E, F, G	0–6	7–8	9–12
H, I, J, K, L, M, N	0–8	9–11	12–15

▶ Circle the rubric according to the total score.

Vocabulary Assessments

Assessing Vocabulary in Context: Level G, Nonfiction
Individual Record

Name _____ Grade _____ Date _____

Bubbles

Check ✓ one: Instructional Level: _____   Independent Level: _____

Vocabulary Word (✓ 4 Words Selected)		Meaning	Student Response
	shiny, p. 4	Bright; giving off light	0 1 2 3
	rainbow, p. 4	An arc of colors	0 1 2 3
	inside, p. 6	In the interior of	0 1 2 3
	filled, p. 6	Full of	0 1 2 3
	air, p. 6	The invisible gases that are all around us	0 1 2 3
	blowing, p. 9	Pushing out a stream of air from the mouth	0 1 2 3
	enormous, p. 12	Very large	0 1 2 3
	pop, p. 16	To burst with a sharp sound	0 1 2 3
		Total Score	

Score:

0 Did not respond or said "I don't know"

1 Made a response that is in some way related to the meaning of the word (any definition of that word)

2 Responded with a definition that is approximately the meaning of the word (same definition of the word as used in the text)

3 Responded with a full definition of the word (precise definition used in the text)

Level	Unsatisfactory	Satisfactory	Excellent
A, B, C	0–4	5–6	7–9
D, E, F, G	0–6	7–8	9–12
H, I, J, K, L, M, N	0–8	9–11	12–15

▶ Circle the rubric according to the total score.

Assessing Vocabulary in Context: Level H, Fiction
Individual Record

Name _____ Grade _____ Date _____

The Sleepover Party

Check ✓ one: Instructional Level: _____   Independent Level: _____

Vocabulary Word (✓ 5 Words Selected)		Meaning	Student Response
	worried, p. 2	Concerned; thinking something bad might happen	0 1 2 3
	invited, p. 3	Asked to attend	0 1 2 3
	pack, p. 4	To put things into a container	0 1 2 3
	listening, p. 5	Paying attention to what someone is saying	0 1 2 3
	thought, p. 5	Had an idea in the mind	0 1 2 3
	favorite, p. 6	Something that is favored or preferred over all others	0 1 2 3
	answered, p. 9	Replied; responded	0 1 2 3
	still, p. 9	Continuing to be; in the same state as a previous time	0 1 2 3
		Total Score	

Score:

0 Did not respond or said "I don't know"

1 Made a response that is in some way related to the meaning of the word (any definition of that word)

2 Responded with a definition that is approximately the meaning of the word (same definition of the word as used in the text)

3 Responded with a full definition of the word (precise definition used in the text)

Level	Unsatisfactory	Satisfactory	Excellent
A, B, C	0–4	5–6	7–9
D, E, F, G	0–6	7–8	9–12
H, I, J, K, L, M, N	0–8	9–11	12–15

▶ Circle the rubric according to the total score.

Vocabulary Assessments

Assessing Vocabulary in Context: Level H, Nonfiction
Individual Record

Name _____   Grade _____   Date _____

Trucks

Check ✓ one: Instructional Level: _____   Independent Level: _____

Vocabulary Word (✓ 5 Words Selected)		Meaning	Student Response
	truck, p. 4	A vehicle for carrying large, heavy things	0 1 2 3
	hose, p. 4	A bendable tube that carries liquid from one place to another	0 1 2 3
	trash, p. 6	Waste; unwanted, leftover items	0 1 2 3
	crushes, p. 6	Squeezes; flattens	0 1 2 3
	carries, p. 6	Brings from one place to another; transports	0 1 2 3
	snowplow, p. 10	A device used to push or carry away snow	0 1 2 3
	market, p. 12	A place where things are bought and sold	0 1 2 3
	work, p. 16	Job; something that needs to be done	0 1 2 3
		Total Score	

Score:

0 Did not respond or said "I don't know"

1 Made a response that is in some way related to the meaning of the word (any definition of that word)

2 Responded with a definition that is approximately the meaning of the word (same definition of the word as used in the text)

3 Responded with a full definition of the word (precise definition used in the text)

Level	Unsatisfactory	Satisfactory	Excellent
A, B, C	0–4	5–6	7–9
D, E, F, G	0–6	7–8	9–12
H, I, J, K, L, M, N	0–8	9–11	12–15

▶ Circle the rubric according to the total score.

Assessing Vocabulary in Context: Level I, Fiction
Individual Record

Name _____ Grade _____ Date _____

The Best Cat

Check ✓ one: Instructional Level: _____   Independent Level: _____

Vocabulary Word (✓ 5 Words Selected)		Meaning	Student Response
	best, p. 2	Better than any others	0 1 2 3
	furry, p. 2	Having lots of fur, or soft hair, covering the body	0 1 2 3
	promise, p. 4	To make a statement that you will do something or behave a certain way	0 1 2 3
	friendly, p. 6	Nice; behaving in a way that is pleasant and kind	0 1 2 3
	everywhere, p. 6	All around; in every place	0 1 2 3
	choose, p. 9	To pick, to select something from a variety of choices	0 1 2 3
	many, p. 14	A large number of	0 1 2 3
	soft, p. 15	Quiet	0 1 2 3
		Total Score	

Score:

0 Did not respond or said "I don't know"

1 Made a response that is in some way related to the meaning of the word (any definition of that word)

2 Responded with a definition that is approximately the meaning of the word (same definition of the word as used in the text)

3 Responded with a full definition of the word (precise definition used in the text)

Level	Unsatisfactory	Satisfactory	Excellent
A, B, C	0–4	5–6	7–9
D, E, F, G	0–6	7–8	9–12
H, I, J, K, L, M, N	0–8	9–11	12–15

▶ Circle the rubric according to the total score.

Vocabulary Assessments

Assessing Vocabulary in Context: Level I, Nonfiction
Individual Record

Name _____   Grade _____   Date _____

All About Koalas

Check ✓ one: Instructional Level: _____   Independent Level: _____

Vocabulary Word (✓ 5 Words Selected)		Meaning	Student Response
	claws, p. 3	Sharp, thin, curved nails on animal's toes	0 1 2 3
	thick, p. 4	Growing close together; dense	0 1 2 3
	fluffy, p. 5	Having lots of soft hair	0 1 2 3
	leaves, p. 6	Thin, flat, green parts that stick out from a plant's stem or shoots	0 1 2 3
	joey, p. 9	A baby koala	0 1 2 3
	special, p. 10	Different from the rest; not ordinary	0 1 2 3
	travels, p. 13	Goes from one place to another	0 1 2 3
	thumbs, p. 13	Short thick fingers set apart from the other fingers on the hand or paw	0 1 2 3
		Total Score	

Score:

0 Did not respond or said "I don't know"

1 Made a response that is in some way related to the meaning of the word (any definition of that word)

2 Responded with a definition that is approximately the meaning of the word (same definition of the word as used in the text)

3 Responded with a full definition of the word (precise definition used in the text)

Level	Unsatisfactory	Satisfactory	Excellent
A, B, C	0–4	5–6	7–9
D, E, F, G	0–6	7–8	9–12
H, I, J, K, L, M, N	0–8	9–11	12–15

▶ Circle the rubric according to the total score.

Assessing Vocabulary in Context: Level J, Fiction
Individual Record

Name _____ Grade _____ Date _____

Our New Neighbors

Check ✓ one: Instructional Level: _____ Independent Level: _____

Vocabulary Word (✓ 5 Words Selected)		Meaning	Student Response
	envelope, p. 2	A piece of folded paper to put a letter in	0 1 2 3
	hope, p. 5	To want or wish for something	0 1 2 3
	corner, p. 6	The place where two sides meet	0 1 2 3
	neighbors, p. 7	People who live nearby	0 1 2 3
	called, p. 7	Spoke in a loud voice	0 1 2 3
	excited, p. 9	Having strong feelings; thrilled	0 1 2 3
	mystery, p. 9	Something that is not known or understood	0 1 2 3
	leaned, p. 14	Tilted toward; rested against	0 1 2 3
		Total Score	

Score:

0 Did not respond or said "I don't know"

1 Made a response that is in some way related to the meaning of the word (any definition of that word)

2 Responded with a definition that is approximately the meaning of the word (same definition of the word as used in the text)

3 Responded with a full definition of the word (precise definition used in the text)

Level	Unsatisfactory	Satisfactory	Excellent
A, B, C	0–4	5–6	7–9
D, E, F, G	0–6	7–8	9–12
H, I, J, K, L, M, N	0–8	9–11	12–15

▶ Circle the rubric according to the total score.

Vocabulary Assessments

Assessing Vocabulary in Context: Level J, Nonfiction
Individual Record

Name _____ Grade _____ Date _____

More Than a Pet

Check ✓ one: Instructional Level: _____   Independent Level: _____

Vocabulary Word (✓ 5 Words Selected)		Meaning	Student Response
	therapy dogs, p. 3	Dogs that help people feel better	0 1 2 3
	service dogs, p. 3	Dogs that work	0 1 2 3
	hospital, p. 4	A place where sick or injured people go to get care	0 1 2 3
	cheer, p. 7	To make happier	0 1 2 3
	visits, p. 8	Sees in order to comfort or help; spends time with	0 1 2 3
	gentle, p. 9	Not harsh or rough; mild	0 1 2 3
	trained, p. 11	Taught	0 1 2 3
	harness, p. 12	Something with straps and fastenings that is placed on an animal	0 1 2 3
		Total Score	

Score:

0   Did not respond or said "I don't know"

1   Made a response that is in some way related to the meaning of the word (any definition of that word)

2   Responded with a definition that is approximately the meaning of the word (same definition of the word as used in the text)

3   Responded with a full definition of the word (precise definition used in the text)

Level	Unsatisfactory	Satisfactory	Excellent
A, B, C	0–4	5–6	7–9
D, E, F, G	0–6	7–8	9–12
H, I, J, K, L, M, N	0–8	9–11	12–15

▶ Circle the rubric according to the total score.

Vocabulary Assessments

Assessing Vocabulary in Context: Level K, Fiction
Individual Record

Name _____ Grade _____ Date _____

Edwin's Haircut

Check ✓ one: Instructional Level: _____ Independent Level: _____

Vocabulary Word (✓ 5 Words Selected)		Meaning	Student Response
	shaggy, p. 2	Having overly long hair	0 1 2 3
	complained, p. 6	Found fault with	0 1 2 3
	crooked, p. 7	Not straight	0 1 2 3
	agreed, p. 7	Had the same opinion	0 1 2 3
	remembered, p. 9	Thought of again	0 1 2 3
	sure, p. 11	Certain; having no doubt	0 1 2 3
	appeared, p. 14	Arrive; came	0 1 2 3
	barber, p. 16	A person who cuts hair	0 1 2 3
		Total Score	

Score:

0 Did not respond or said "I don't know"

1 Made a response that is in some way related to the meaning of the word (any definition of that word)

2 Responded with a definition that is approximately the meaning of the word (same definition of the word as used in the text)

3 Responded with a full definition of the word (precise definition used in the text)

Level	Unsatisfactory	Satisfactory	Excellent
A, B, C	0–4	5–6	7–9
D, E, F, G	0–6	7–8	9–12
H, I, J, K, L, M, N	0–8	9–11	12–15

▶ Circle the rubric according to the total score.

Vocabulary Assessments

Assessing Vocabulary in Context: Level K, Nonfiction
Individual Record

Name _____   Grade _____   Date _____

Surprising Animal Senses

Check ✓ one: Instructional Level: _____   Independent Level: _____

Vocabulary Word (✓ 5 Words Selected)		Meaning	Student Response
	senses, p. 2	The body's way of taking in stimuli; sight, smell, hearing, touch, and taste	0 1 2 3
	starfish, p. 5	A sea animal with arms that extend from the center, to make a star shape	0 1 2 3
	rough, p. 6	Having a surface that is uneven; not smooth	0 1 2 3
	sandpaper, p. 6	Paper with rough material glued to it, intended to be rubbed on a surface to make the surface smooth	0 1 2 3
	whiskers, p. 7	Long, thick hairs growing on an animal	0 1 2 3
	openings, p. 7	Holes; open places; spaces to pass through	0 1 2 3
	whisper, p. 12	To talk in a low, soft voice	0 1 2 3
	track, p. 15	To follow the tracks of something or someone	0 1 2 3
		Total Score	

Score:

0   Did not respond or said "I don't know"

1   Made a response that is in some way related to the meaning of the word (any definition of that word)

2   Responded with a definition that is approximately the meaning of the word (same definition of the word as used in the text)

3   Responded with a full definition of the word (precise definition used in the text)

Level	Unsatisfactory	Satisfactory	Excellent
A, B, C	0–4	5–6	7–9
D, E, F, G	0–6	7–8	9–12
H, I, J, K, L, M, N	0–8	9–11	12–15

▶ Circle the rubric according to the total score.

Assessing Vocabulary in Context: Level L, Fiction
Individual Record

Name _____ Grade _____ Date _____

Dog Stories

Check ✓ one: Instructional Level: _____ Independent Level: _____

Vocabulary Word (✓ 5 Words Selected)		Meaning	Student Response
	author, p. 5	A person who writes a book or story	0 1 2 3
	wonderful, p. 7	Great; very special	0 1 2 3
	hero, p. 7	The most important character in a story	0 1 2 3
	photograph, p. 8	A picture taken by a camera	0 1 2 3
	warned, p. 8	To let know ahead of time	0 1 2 3
	leash, p. 10	A strap or chain that is used to keep a dog close by	0 1 2 3
	dove, p. 10	Jumped into; plunged	0 1 2 3
	dangling, p. 10	Hanging	0 1 2 3
	addressed, p. 14	Directed to; having someone's address	0 1 2 3
	disappointed, p. 15	Let down	0 1 2 3
		Total Score	

Score:

0 Did not respond or said "I don't know"

1 Made a response that is in some way related to the meaning of the word (any definition of that word)

2 Responded with a definition that is approximately the meaning of the word (same definition of the word as used in the text)

3 Responded with a full definition of the word (precise definition used in the text)

Vocabulary Assessments

Level	Unsatisfactory	Satisfactory	Excellent
A, B, C	0–4	5–6	7–9
D, E, F, G	0–6	7–8	9–12
H, I, J, K, L, M, N	0–8	9–11	12–15

▶ Circle the rubric according to the total score.

Assessing Vocabulary in Context: Level L, Nonfiction
Individual Record

Name _____   Grade _____   Date _____

Giants of the Sea

Check ✓ one: Instructional Level: _____   Independent Level: _____

Vocabulary Word (✓ 5 Words Selected)		Meaning	Student Response
	underwater, p. 6	Below the surface of the water	0 1 2 3
	lungs, p. 7	An organ in the chest that is used for breathing	0 1 2 3
	blowholes, p. 7	Hole found on the top of whales' heads, used for breathing	0 1 2 3
	spray, p. 8	A mist of tiny drops	0 1 2 3
	dive, p. 9	To plunge headfirst into water	0 1 2 3
	surface, p. 10	The outside or top of something	0 1 2 3
	communicate, p. 12	To exchange information	0 1 2 3
	whistle, p. 12	To make a high-pitched sound by blowing	0 1 2 3
	bounce, p. 13	To hit against a surface and come back	0 1 2 3
	orca, p. 15	Killer whale	0 1 2 3
		Total Score	

Score:

0 Did not respond or said "I don't know"

1 Made a response that is in some way related to the meaning of the word (any definition of that word)

2 Responded with a definition that is approximately the meaning of the word (same definition of the word as used in the text)

3 Responded with a full definition of the word (precise definition used in the text)

Level	Unsatisfactory	Satisfactory	Excellent
A, B, C	0–4	5–6	7–9
D, E, F, G	0–6	7–8	9–12
H, I, J, K, L, M, N	0–8	9–11	12–15

▶ Circle the rubric according to the total score.

Assessing Vocabulary in Context: Level M, Fiction
Individual Record

Name _____ Grade _____ Date _____

The Thing About Nathan

Check ✓ one: Instructional Level: _____   Independent Level: _____

Vocabulary Word (✓ 5 Words Selected)		Meaning	Student Response
	herd, p. 2	A group of the same kind of animals all living together	0 1 2 3
	neat, p. 3	Tidy; clean; orderly	0 1 2 3
	trade, p. 4	Swap; exchange one thing for another	0 1 2 3
	supposed, p. 4	To have to do something; to be required	0 1 2 3
	bursting, p. 6	Filled to the breaking point	0 1 2 3
	kits, p. 6	Sets of parts or pieces that are to be put together	0 1 2 3
	declared, p. 7	Said in a formal way	0 1 2 3
	tossing, p. 12	Throwing lightly	0 1 2 3
	seriously, p. 13	To a great degree; extremely	0 1 2 3
	described, p. 15	Told in detail	0 1 2 3
		Total Score	

Score:

0 Did not respond or said "I don't know"

1 Made a response that is in some way related to the meaning of the word (any definition of that word)

2 Responded with a definition that is approximately the meaning of the word (same definition of the word as used in the text)

3 Responded with a full definition of the word (precise definition used in the text)

Level	Unsatisfactory	Satisfactory	Excellent
A, B, C	0–4	5–6	7–9
D, E, F, G	0–6	7–8	9–12
H, I, J, K, L, M, N	0–8	9–11	12–15

▶ Circle the rubric according to the total score.

Vocabulary Assessments

Assessing Vocabulary in Context: Level M, Nonfiction
Individual Record

Name _____ Grade _____ Date _____

The Life of a Monarch Butterfly

Check ✓ one: Instructional Level: _____   Independent Level: _____

Vocabulary Word (✓ 5 Words Selected)		Meaning	Student Response
	speck, p. 2	A small spot	0 1 2 3
	tiny, p. 2	Very small	0 1 2 3
	female, p. 3	Being the gender that gives birth	0 1 2 3
	hatch, p. 4	To come out of the egg	0 1 2 3
	expecting, p. 4	Thinking something will happen	0 1 2 3
	tight, p. 5	Fitting too closely	0 1 2 3
	underneath, p. 6	Directly below or under	0 1 2 3
	chrysalis, p. 8	The covering that protects a young moth or butterfly	0 1 2 3
	clings, p. 12	Holds on tightly to something	0 1 2 3
	flutter, p. 15	To move the wings quickly	0 1 2 3
		Total Score	

Score:

0 Did not respond or said "I don't know"

1 Made a response that is in some way related to the meaning of the word (any definition of that word)

2 Responded with a definition that is approximately the meaning of the word (same definition of the word as used in the text)

3 Responded with a full definition of the word (precise definition used in the text)

Level	Unsatisfactory	Satisfactory	Excellent
A, B, C	0–4	5–6	7–9
D, E, F, G	0–6	7–8	9–12
H, I, J, K, L, M, N	0–8	9–11	12–15

▶ Circle the rubric according to the total score.

Assessing Vocabulary in Context: Level N, Fiction
Individual Record

Name _____ Grade _____ Date _____

The Big Snow

Check ✓ one: Instructional Level: _____   Independent Level: _____

Vocabulary Word (✓ 5 Words Selected)		Meaning	Student Response
	finally, p. 2	Happening at the end of a period of time	0 1 2 3
	ankle-deep, p. 2	Having a depth just above the top of the feet	0 1 2 3
	apartment, p. 3	A room or rooms used as a home	0 1 2 3
	pretend, p. 3	To make believe	0 1 2 3
	vanished, p. 4	Disappeared, or passed from sight	0 1 2 3
	ignore, p. 6	To not pay attention to	0 1 2 3
	uneasy, p. 6	Not comfortable; worried	0 1 2 3
	nervous, p. 8	Fearful; worried	0 1 2 3
	elevator, p. 11	A small room used to carry people or things up and down from one floor of a building to another	0 1 2 3
	exhausted, p. 15	Tired; out of energy	0 1 2 3
		Total Score	

Score:

0 Did not respond or said "I don't know"

1 Made a response that is in some way related to the meaning of the word (any definition of that word)

2 Responded with a definition that is approximately the meaning of the word (same definition of the word as used in the text)

3 Responded with a full definition of the word (precise definition used in the text)

Level	Unsatisfactory	Satisfactory	Excellent
A, B, C	0–4	5–6	7–9
D, E, F, G	0–6	7–8	9–12
H, I, J, K, L, M, N	0–8	9–11	12–15

▶ Circle the rubric according to the total score.

Vocabulary Assessments

Assessing Vocabulary in Context: Level N, Nonfiction
Individual Record

Name _____ Grade _____ Date _____

Exploring Caves

Check ✓ one: Instructional Level: _____   Independent Level: _____

Vocabulary Word (✓ 5 Words Selected)		Meaning	Student Response
	caverns, p. 2	Large caves	0 1 2 3
	invisible, p. 4	Not able to be seen	0 1 2 3
	seeps, p. 4	Moves slowly through small cracks or spaces	0 1 2 3
	continues, p. 5	Carries on; keeps going	0 1 2 3
	sites, p. 6	Places where a particular thing is located or can be found	0 1 2 3
	experts, p. 6	People who know a lot about a subject or have a special skill	0 1 2 3
	prepared, p. 7	To be ready for something	0 1 2 3
	sturdy, p. 7	Strong and well made or built	0 1 2 3
	entrances, p. 11	Ways into something	0 1 2 3
	columns, p. 14	Tall, vertical, round posts	0 1 2 3
		Total Score	

Score:

0 Did not respond or said "I don't know"

1 Made a response that is in some way related to the meaning of the word (any definition of that word)

2 Responded with a definition that is approximately the meaning of the word (same definition of the word as used in the text)

3 Responded with a full definition of the word (precise definition used in the text)

Level	Unsatisfactory	Satisfactory	Excellent
A, B, C	0–4	5–6	7–9
D, E, F, G	0–6	7–8	9–12
H, I, J, K, L, M, N	0–8	9–11	12–15

▶ Circle the rubric according to the total score.

Vocabulary Assessments

Resources

In this section, you will find a variety of helpful forms and tools that are referenced in the *Benchmark Assessment Guide*. You can photocopy the pages from this book or print them from the *Forms CD-ROM*.

Assessment at-a-Glance

Preparation

Materials

▶ Benchmark Books

▶ Recording Forms

▶ Student Writing Materials

▶ F&P Calculator/Stopwatch.

▶ Assessment Summary Form

Administration

1. **Record** student information on the Recording Form.

2. Read the **title** and the **introduction** to the student.

3. Start the **timer** (Start Time) on the calculator. *

4. Have the student start **reading orally.**

5. **Code** the reading behavior on the form.

6. Stop the **timer** (End Time) on the calculator and record the time on the form. *

7. Enter number of **running words (RW)**, **errors (#Errors)**, and **self-corrections** (#**SC**) on the calculator.

8. Make brief notes about **fluency** and/or circle a fluency rating.

9. Have a **conversation** with the student about the text. Use prompts as needed and score each area.

10. Press buttons (**Accur. %, SC, WPM**) to obtain and record scores.

11. Repeat the process until you have determined **independent, instructional,** and **hard** text level.

12. **Record** the results on the Assessment Summary Form.

* Only if calculating rate, recommended at Level J and above.

Coding and Scoring Errors at-a-Glance

Behavior	What the Reader Does	How to Code	Example	How to Score	
Accurate Reading	Reads words correctly	Do not mark or place check (✓) above word.	no mark or $\frac{✓}{Kate}$		No error
Substitution	Gives an incorrect response.	Write the substituted word above the word.	$\frac{her}{Kate's}$	Substitution, not corrected	1 error
				Substitution, self-corrected (SC)	No error; 1 SC
Multiple Substitutions	Makes several attempts at a word	Write each of the substitutions in sequence above the word.	$\frac{little|some|him}{his}$	Multiple substitutions, not corrected	1 error for each incorrect word in text
			$\frac{touch|teeth|SC}{tooth}$	Multiple substitutions, self-corrected (SC)	No error; 1 SC
			$\frac{to|touch|teeth}{tooth}$	Multiple misreadings of the same word not corrected	1 error for each incorrect word in text
			$\frac{Kathy|Kelly}{Kate}$	Multiple misreadings of names and proper nouns	1 error first time missed; no errors after that
			$\frac{It's}{It is}$ $\frac{Do\ not}{Don't}$	Misreading contractions (reads contraction as two words or two words as contraction)	1 error each time
Self-correction	Corrects a previous error	Write the error over the word, followed by SC.	$\frac{teeth|SC}{tooth}$		No error; 1 SC
Insertion	Adds a word that is not in the text	Write in the inserted word using a carat (^).	loose ⌃		1 error per word inserted
Omission	Gives no response to a word	Place a dash (–) above the word.	$\frac{-}{Very}$	Skipping a word	1 error per word
				Skipping a line	1 error per word
Repetition	Reads the same word again	Write R above the word.	R		No error

Coding system developed by Marie Clay as part of the running record system in An Observation Survey of Early Literacy Achievement, *Revised Second Edition, 2006, Heinemann.*

Resources

Coding and Scoring Errors at-a-Glance (continued)

Behavior	What the Reader Does	How to Code	Example	How to Score	
Repeated Repetitions	Reads the same word more than once	Write R above the word for the first repetition and then write a number for the additional repetitions.	R₂ R₃		No error
Rereading	Returns to the beginning of sentence or phrase to read again	Write R with an arrow back to the place where rereading began.	R		No error
	Rereads and self-corrects	Write R with an arrow back to the place where rereading began and SC at point of self-correction	tooth to come|SC ^R tooth to fall		No error; 1 SC
Appeal	Verbally asks for help	Write A above the word.	$\frac{A}{very}$	Follow up with "You try it."	No error
"You Try It"	The child appeals, the teacher responds with "You try it."	Write Y after the word.	$\frac{A}{very}$ | Y	"You try it" followed by correct word	No error
				"You try it" followed by omission, incorrect word, or Told	1 error
Told	Child doesn't attempt word even after "You try it."	Write T after the word or the Y.	$\frac{A}{very}$|Y|T $\frac{A}{very}$|T		1 error
Spelling Aloud	The child spells the word by saying the names of letters.	Write the letters in all capital letters.	$\frac{B\text{-}U\text{-}T}{But}$	Spelling followed by correct word	No error
				Spelling followed by incorrect word	1 error
Sounding Out	The child makes the sounds associated with the letters in the word.	Write the letters in lowercase with hyphens between them.	$\frac{n\text{-}o\text{-}t}{not}$	"Sounding out" followed by correct word	No error; no SC
			$\frac{l\text{-}o\text{-}s}{loose}$ |lose	"Sounding out" followed by incorrect word	1 error
			$\frac{f\text{-}}{come}$ | SC	Sounding the first letter incorrectly and then saying the word correctly	No error; 1 SC

Coding system developed by Marie Clay as part of the running record system in An Observation Survey of Early Literacy Achievement, Revised Second Edition, *2006, Heinemann.*

Resources

Name: _____ Date: _____

© 2011, 2008 by Irene C. Fountas and Gay Su Pinnell. Portsmouth, NH: Heinemann. This page may be photocopied.

Key: C=Consistent
P=Partial
N=Not evident

Guide for Observing and Noting Reading Behaviors	C P N	Notes
1. Early Reading Behaviors *Does the reader:* • Move left to right across a line of print? • Return to the left for a new line? • Match voice to print while reading a line or more of print? • Recognize a few easy high-frequency words?		
2. Searching for and Using Information **Meaning** *Does the reader:* • Make meaningful attempts at unknown words? • Use the meaning of the story or text to predict unknown words? • Reread to gather more information to solve a word? • Reread and use the meaning of the sentence? • Reread to search for more details—information, characters, plot? • Reread to gather information to clarify confusions? • Use headings and titles to think about the meaning of a section of text? • Use information in the pictures to help in understanding a text? • Use knowledge of the genre (and its characteristics) to help in understanding a text? • Use knowledge of the genre (and its characteristics) to help in finding information? • Use readers' tools to help in finding information (glossary, index)? **Structure** *Does the reader:* • Use knowledge of oral language to solve unknown words? • Reread to see if a word "sounds right" in a sentence? • Reread to correct using language structure? **Visual Information** *Does the reader:* • Use the visual information to solve words? • Use the sound of the first letter(s) to attempt or solve a word? • Use some, most, or all of the visual information to solve words? • Use sound analysis to solve a word? • Make attempts that are visually similar? • Use knowledge of a high-frequency word to problem solve? • Search for more visual information within a word to solve it? • Use analogy to solve unknown words? • Use syllables to solve words? • Use prefixes and suffixes to take apart and recognize words? • Use inflectional endings to problem solve words? • Recognize words quickly and easily? • Reread and use the sound of the first letter to solve a word? • Problem solve unknown words quickly and efficiently? • Work actively to solve words? • Use multiple sources of information together in attempts at words? • Use all sources of information flexibly to solve words? • Use all sources of information in an orchestrated way?		
3. Solving Words *Does the reader:* • Recognize a core of high-frequency words quickly? • Recognize words quickly and easily? • Use a variety of flexible ways to take words apart? • Use the meaning of the sentences to solve words? • Use the structure of the sentence to solve words? • Use some of the visual information to solve words? • Use known word parts to solve words?		

Guide for Observing . . . (cont.)	C P N	Notes
3. Solving Words *(cont.)* *Does the reader:* • Use sound analysis (sounding out)? • Use analogy to solve words? • Make attempts that are visually similar? • Use the sound of the first letter to solve words? • Work actively to solve words? • Use known words or parts to solve unknown words? • Use syllables to problem solve? • Use prefixes and suffixes to take words apart? • Use inflectional endings to take words apart? • Use sentence context to derive the meaning of words? • Use base words and root words to derive the meaning of words? • Make connections among words to understand their meaning?		
4. Self-Monitoring *Does the reader:* • Hesitate at an unknown word? • Stop at an unknown word? • Stop at an unknown word and appeal for help? • Stop after an error? • Notice mismatches? • Notice when an attempt does not look right? • Notice when an attempt does not sound right? • Notice when an attempt does not make sense? • Reread to confirm reading? • Use knowledge of some high-frequency words to check on reading? • Check one source of information with another? • Check an attempt that makes sense with language? • Check an attempt that makes sense with the letters (visual information)? • Use language structure to check on reading? • Request help after making several attempts?		
5. Self-Correcting *Does the reader:* • Reread and try again until accurate? • Stop after an error and make another attempt? • Stop after an error and make multiple attempts until accurate? • Reread to self-correct? • Work actively to solve mismatches? • Self-correct errors?		
6. Maintaining Fluency *Does the reader:* • Read without pointing? • Read word groups (phrases)? • Put words together? • Read smoothly? • Read the punctuation? • Make the voice go down at periods? • Make the voice go up at question marks? • Pause briefly at commas, dashes, and hyphens? • Read dialogue with intonation or expression? • Stress the appropriate words to convey accurate meaning? • Read at a good rate—not too fast and not too slow?		
7. Other Behaviors		

Resources

Scoring and Analysis at-a-Glance

Score Part I Oral Reading on the Recording Form scoring page

1. **Accuracy Rate** Circle the number of errors on the graph to determine the percent of words read correctly.

2. **Self-Correction Ratio** Number of errors + Number of self-corrections [÷] = 1: ___

3. **Fluency Score** Circle a score.

4. **Reading Rate** Record or calculate the words per minute (WPM) read. Number of timed seconds read [÷] Number of running words [×] 60 = WPM

Score Part II Comprehension Conversation with the key understandings chart on the Recording Form
5. **Comprehension Conversation**

   a. Assign points in each category (Within, Beyond, About the text)

   b. Total the category scores, adding a point if appropriate for additional understandings, and circle the final evaluation in the Guide to Total Score box.

Score Part III Writing About Reading (optional) on the Recording Form

6. Circle the appropriate score on the scoring key.

Complete the Assessment Summary.

7. Record data from the Recording Form on the Assessment Summary form.

8. Determine two Benchmark Levels and write them in the box in the upper right corner of the Assessment Summary.

Benchmark Independent Level
Levels A–K: 95–100% accuracy with excellent or satisfactory comprehension
Levels L–Z: 98–100% accuracy with excellent or satisfactory comprehension

Benchmark Instructional Level
Levels A–K: 90–94% accuracy with excellent or satisfactory comprehension or 95–100% accuracy with limited comprehension
Levels L–Z: 95–97% accuracy with excellent or satisfactory comprehension or 98–100% accuracy with limited comprehension

9. Review accuracy, use of sources of information, problem solving, self-correction ratio, fluency, and comprehension to determine Recommended Placement Level.

10. Use the Guide for Observing and Noting Reading Behaviors (in the *Assessment Guide* and *Assessment Forms* book and CD-ROM) to make additional comments and make notes about instructional implications at the bottom of the Assessment Summary form.

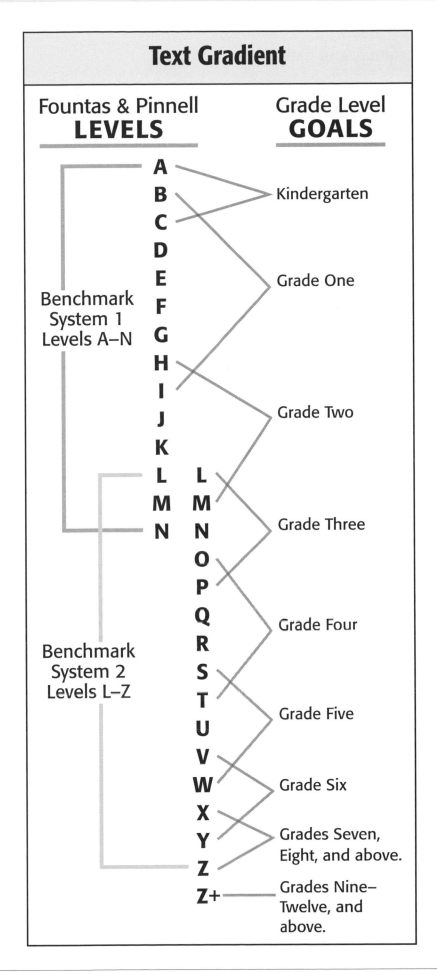

Text Gradient

Fountas & Pinnell LEVELS

Grade Level GOALS

A
B
C
D
E
F
G
H
I
J
K
L
M
N

Benchmark System 1 Levels A–N

L
M
N
O
P
Q
R
S
T
U
V
W
X
Y
Z
Z+

Benchmark System 2 Levels L–Z

Kindergarten

Grade One

Grade Two

Grade Three

Grade Four

Grade Five

Grade Six

Grades Seven, Eight, and above.

Grades Nine–Twelve, and above.

Resources

Finding Easy, Instructional, and Hard Texts

If the first book is…	Then…
Easy **Levels A–K:** Student reads at 95–100% accuracy with excellent or satisfactory comprehension. **Levels L–N:** Student reads at 98–100% accuracy with excellent or satisfactory comprehension.	Move to a higher level text and repeat the same process until the student reads a text that is hard.
Instructional **Levels A–K:** Student reads at 90-94% accuracy with excellent or satisfactory comprehension or 95-100% accuracy with limited comprehension. **Levels L–N**: Student reads at 95–97% accuracy with excellent or satisfactory comprehension or 98–100% accuracy with limited comprehension.	Move to a lower level text and repeat the same process until the student reads a text that is easy and move to a higher level text until the student reads a text that is hard.
Hard **Levels A–K**: Student reads below 90% accuracy with any score on comprehension. **Levels L–N**: Student reads below 95% accuracy with any score on comprehension.	Move to a lower level text and repeat the same process until the student reads a text at an instructional level.